✔ KU-540-159

## The aims

The specification aims to:
- stimulate and sustain students' interest in, and enjoyment of, chemistry
- enable students to gain a knowledge and understanding of chemistry appropriate to these levels and to appreciate the interlinking patterns which are a distinguishing feature of the subject
- show the interrelationship between the development of the subject and its application (social, economic, environmental and technological) and recognise the value of chemistry to society and how it may be used responsibly
- develop skills in laboratory procedures and techniques, carry these out with due regard for safety and assess the uses and limitations of the procedures
- foster imaginative and critical thinking as well as the acquisition of knowledge, together with an appreciation of the intellectual discipline which the subject provides
- develop students' ability to acquire knowledge by means of practical work
- provide opportunities for students to bring together knowledge of how different areas of chemistry relate to each other
- provide an appropriate course for those who will end their study of the subject at one of these stages as well as laying a secure foundation for those who will continue their studies in this or related subjects

# The unit test

The unit test consists of a structured question paper of duration 1 hour, worth 60 marks. This counts for 30% of AS or 15% of Advanced GCE marks.

Unit Test 2 has two assessment objectives:
- AO1 is 'knowledge with understanding' and makes up two-thirds of the test. You should be able to:
  - recognise, recall and show understanding of specific chemical facts, principles, concepts, practical techniques and terminology
  - draw on existing knowledge to show understanding of the responsible use of chemistry in society
  - select, organise and present information clearly and logically, using specialist vocabulary where appropriate
- AO2 is 'application of knowledge and understanding, analysis, synthesis and evaluation' and makes up one-third of Unit Test 2. You should be able to:
  - describe, explain and interpret phenomena and effects in terms of chemical principles and concepts
  - present arguments and ideas clearly and logically, using specialist vocabulary where appropriate
  - interpret and translate, from one form into another, data presented as continuous prose or in tables, diagrams and graphs

- carry out calculations
- apply chemical principles and concepts to unfamiliar situations including those related to the responsible use of chemistry in society
- assess the validity of chemical information, experiments, inferences and statements

The following command terms are used in the specification and in unit test questions. You must distinguish between them carefully.

- **Recall** — a simple remembering of facts learned, without any explanation or justification of these facts
- **Understand** — be able to explain the relationship between facts and underlying chemical principles (understanding enables you to use facts in new situations)
- **Predict** — say what you think will happen on the basis of learned principles
- **Define** — give a simple definition, without any explanation
- **Determine** — find out
- **Show** — relate one set of facts to another set
- **Interpret** — take data or other types of information and use them to construct chemical theories or principles
- **Describe** — state the characteristics of a particular material or thing
- **Explain** — use chemical theories or principles to say why a particular property of a substance or series of substances is as it is

# Learning to learn

Learning is not instinctive — you have to develop suitable techniques to make your use of time effective. In particular, chemistry has peculiar difficulties that need to be understood if your studies are to be effective from the start.

## Planning

Busy people do not achieve what they do by approaching their life haphazardly. They plan — so that if they are working they mean to be working, and if they are watching TV they have planned to do so. Planning is essential. You must know what you have to do each day and set aside time to do it. Furthermore, to devote time to study means you may have to give something up that you are already doing. There is no way that you can generate extra hours in the day.

Be realistic in your planning. You cannot work all the time, and you must build in time for recreation and family responsibilities.

## Targets

When devising your plan, have a target for each study period. This might be a particular section of the specification, or it might be rearranging of information from text into pictures, or the construction of a flowchart relating all the organic reactions you need to know. Whatever it is, be determined to master your target material before you leave it.

# Reading chemistry textbooks

A page of chemistry has material of widely differing difficulty which requires different levels and styles of effort in order to master it. Therefore, the speed at which the various parts of a page can be read is variable. In addition, you should read with pencil and paper to hand and jot things down as you go, for example equations, diagrams and questions to be followed up. If you do not note the questions, you will forget them; if you do not master detail, you will never become fluent in chemistry.

### Text
This is the easiest part to read, and little advice is needed here.

### Chemical equations
Equations are used because they are quantitative, concise and internationally understood. Take time over them, copy them and check that they balance. Most of all, try to visualise what is happening as the reaction proceeds. If you can't, make a note to ask someone who can or — even better — ask your teacher to *show* you the reaction if at all possible. Equations describe real processes; they are not abstract algebraic constructs.

### Graphs
Graphs give a lot of information, and they must be understood in detail rather than as a general impression. Take time over them. Note what the axes are, what the units are, the shape of the graph and what the shape means in chemical terms.

### Tables
These are a means of displaying a lot of information. You need to be aware of the table headings and the units of numerical entries. Take time over them. What trends can be seen? How do these relate to chemical properties? Sometimes it can be useful to convert tables of data into graphs.

### Diagrams
Diagrams of apparatus should be drawn in section. When you see them, copy them and ask yourself why the apparatus has the features it has. What is the difference between a distillation and a reflux apparatus, for example? When you do practical work, examine each piece of the apparatus closely so that you know both its form and function.

### Mathematical equations
In chemistry, mathematical equations describe the real, physical world. If you do not understand what an equation means, ask someone who does.

### Calculations
Do not take calculations on trust — work through them. First, make certain that you understand the problem, and then that you understand each step in the solution. Make

clear the units of the physical quantities used and make sure you understand the underlying chemistry. If you have problems, ask.

Always make a note of problems and questions that you need to ask your teacher. Learning is not a contest or a trial. Nobody has ever learnt anything without effort or without running into difficulties from time to time — not even your teachers.

## Notes

Most people have notes of some sort. Notes can take many forms: they might be permanent or temporary; they might be lists, diagrams or flowcharts. You have to develop your own styles — note the plural. For example, notes that are largely words can often be recast into charts or pictures and this is useful for imprinting the material. The more you rework the material, the clearer it will become.

Whatever form your notes take, they must be organised. Notes that are not indexed or filed properly are useless, as are notes written at enormous length and those written so cryptically that they are unintelligible a month later.

## Writing

In chemistry, particularly in the early unit tests, extended writing is not often required. However, you need to be able to write concisely and accurately. This requires you to marshal your thoughts properly and needs to be practised during your ordinary learning.

Have your ideas assembled in your head before you start to write. You might imagine them as a list of bullet points. Before you write, have an idea of how you are going to link these points together and also how your answer will end. The space available for an answer is a poor guide to the amount that you have to write — handwriting sizes differ hugely, as does the ability to write crisply. Filling the space does not necessarily mean you have answered the question. The mark allocation suggests the number of points to be made, not the amount of writing needed.

### Re-reading

When you have completed your work, you must re-read it critically. This is remarkably difficult, because you tend to read what you intended to write rather than what you actually did write. Nevertheless, time spent on the evaluation of your own work is time well spent. You should be able to eliminate at least the majority of silly errors — but you need to practise this in your ordinary work and not do it for the first time in an examination.

# Approaching the unit test

The unit test is designed to allow you to show the examiner what you know. Answering questions successfully is not only a matter of knowing the chemistry but is also a matter of technique. Unit Test 2 is a paper with structured questions only, which are answered on the question paper.

## Revision

- Start your revision in plenty of time. Make a list of the things that you need to do, emphasising the things that you find most difficult — and draw up a detailed revision plan. Work back from the examination date, ideally leaving an entire week free from fresh revision before that date. Be realistic in your revision plan and then add 25% to the timings because everything takes longer than you think.
- When revising, make a note of difficulties and ask your teacher about them. If you do not make these notes you will forget to ask.
- Make use of past papers, but remember that these will have been written to a different specification.
- Revise ideas, rather than forms of words — you are after *understanding*.
- Scholarship requires time to be spent on the work.
- When you use the example questions in this book, make a determined effort to answer them before looking up the answers and comments.
- Remember that the answers here are not intended as model answers to be learnt parrot-fashion. They are answers designed to illuminate chemical ideas and understanding.

## The exam

- *Read the question*. Questions usually change from one examination to the next. A question that looks the same, at a cursory glance, to one that you have seen before usually has significant differences when read carefully. Needless to say, candidates do not receive credit for writing answers to their own questions.
- Be aware of the number of marks available for a question. That is an excellent pointer to the number of things you need to say.
- Do not repeat the question in your answer. We can all see the question. The danger is that you then fill up the space available and think that you have answered the question, when in reality some or maybe all of the real points have been ignored.
- The name of a 'rule' is not an explanation for a chemical phenomenon. Thus, in equilibrium, a popular answer to a question on the effect of a change of pressure on an equilibrium system is 'Because of Le Chatelier's principle...'. That is simply a name for a rule — it does not explain anything.
- Even though all the questions in the unit test have to be answered, it is worth looking through the whole paper before you start to write. A great deal of subconscious thinking can be triggered, which will make things slightly easier when you do come to write. It's worth knowing what's around the corner.

Content
Guidance

**T**his section is a guide to the content of **Unit 2: Introductory Organic Chemistry, Energetics, Kinetics and Equilibrium and Applications**. It does not constitute a textbook for Unit 2 material.

The main areas of this unit are:
- Energetics — Hess's law
- Organic chemistry — introduction, alkanes, alkenes, halogenoalkanes and alcohols
- Kinetics — qualitative
- Chemical equilibria — qualitative
- Industrial inorganic chemistry — Haber process, Contact process and the extraction of aluminium

For each part of the specification, you should also consult a standard textbook for more information. Chemistry is a subtle subject, and you need to have a good sense of where the information you are dealing with fits into the larger chemical landscape. This only comes by reading. Remember that the specification tells you only what can be examined in the unit test.

# Energetics

## Enthalpy change

The heat change ($\Delta H$) that occurs during a chemical reaction at constant pressure (i.e. in a vessel open to the atmosphere) is called the **enthalpy change** for that reaction. It is measured in $kJ\,mol^{-1}$, where '$mol^{-1}$' refers to the molar quantities given in the equation. Therefore

$$2SO_2(g) + O_2(g) \longrightarrow 2SO_3(g) \quad \Delta H = -92\,kJ\,mol^{-1}$$

means that 92 kJ of heat are given out when two moles of sulphur dioxide combine with one mole of oxygen to give two moles of sulphur trioxide. Such an equation is called a **thermochemical** equation.

Note that an enthalpy change should not be called an energy change. Energy changes during reactions are calculated at constant volume and the values obtained are not necessarily the same as the enthalpy change for the reaction.

Changes of state, for example from liquid to gas or from solid to liquid, are accompanied by heat changes. The states of the substances in the reaction are important. The combustion of, for instance, methane would give out more energy if the product water were liquid rather than gaseous, the difference being the enthalpy of vaporisation of the liquid water. Thermochemical equations are commonly shown for substances in their **standard state**, the associated enthalpy changes being standard enthalpies and this being shown by the superscript symbol '$\ominus$', i.e. $\Delta H^{\ominus}$.

Standard conditions mean:

- all reagents and products are in their thermodynamically most stable state
- 1 atmosphere pressure
- a specified temperature

The value of the temperature is not part of the definition of standard conditions. In practice, if no temperature is shown the default value is 298 K (25 °C). Some older British data give it as 291 K (18 °C).

Some elements have different forms (allotropes) in the solid state. For carbon, it is necessary to specify graphite or diamond rather than just solid (s).

## Exothermic and endothermic reactions

Heat may be given out or taken in during a chemical reaction. The international convention is that heat changes are seen from the point of view of the chemical system — imagine you are sitting inside the reaction mixture.

- Heat *taken in* is regarded as positive; so endothermic processes have a *positive* $\Delta H$.
- Heat *given out* is regarded as negative, so exothermic processes have a *negative* $\Delta H$.

Note that the positive or negative signs represent *conventions* concerning the direction of heat flow. They do not represent relative magnitudes in the same way that plus or minus signs do with numbers. Suppose that for one reaction $\Delta H$ is $-100\,kJ\,mol^{-1}$, and that for another reaction $\Delta H$ is $-200\,kJ\,mol^{-1}$. The second value is not smaller than the first — indeed, it represents twice as much heat given out. Instead of using the terms 'smaller' or 'larger', which are always ambiguous, use 'more exothermic' or whatever is appropriate.

## Definitions

### Standard enthalpy of formation, $\Delta H_f$
The heat change for the formation of one mole of substance from its elements, all substances being in their most stable state at 1 atm pressure and a specified temperature.

### Standard enthalpy of combustion, $\Delta H_c$
The heat change when one mole of substance is completely burnt in excess oxygen, all substances being in their most stable state at 1 atm pressure and a specified temperature.

### Standard enthalpy of neutralisation, $\Delta H_{neut}$
The heat change when an acid is neutralised by an alkali, to produce one mole of water at 1 atm pressure and a specified temperature.

Strictly speaking, the concentration of the solutions should also be specified when dealing with the standard state, but this refinement is unnecessary for present purposes.

## Enthalpy level diagrams

Enthalpy level diagrams show the relative energy levels of reactants and products. The horizontal axis is often absent, unlabelled, or may be called the 'reaction coordinate'. Enthalpy level diagrams for exothermic and endothermic reactions are shown below.

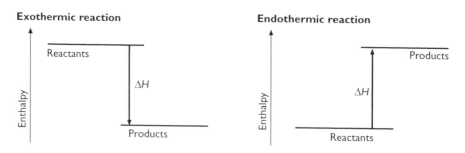

## Direction of spontaneous change

The sign of the enthalpy change does not always indicate the direction of spontaneous change. *A detailed understanding of this is not required by the specification*, but it is the single most important idea in the whole of physical chemistry, since it explains why chemical reactions occur.

- A spontaneous change is one that occurs without external influence to drive it; the conditions of temperature need to be specified.
- Spontaneity is a thermodynamic idea; the rate of a spontaneous reaction may be very slow. Thus, the oxidation of methane to carbon dioxide and water is a spontaneous reaction at room temperature because it is thermodynamically feasible. It does not occur at an observable rate because the activation energy for the reaction is too high for sufficient molecular collisions that exceed this energy to occur.
- There are some reactions that occur spontaneously that are also endothermic, with a positive value of $\Delta H$. An example is the reaction between nitrogen and oxygen:

$$N_2(g) + O_2(g) \longrightarrow 2NO(g) \quad \Delta H = +90\, kJ\, mol^{-1}$$

  Since the heat content of the system is higher after the reaction than before, the minimising of heat content cannot be a criterion for spontaneity.
- The enthalpy change for a reaction is only one of two factors that determine whether that reaction is spontaneous; the other factor is the **entropy change**, $\Delta S$, a quantity that can be equated roughly with the change in the disorder of a system.
- The overall quantity that determines spontaneity is the **Gibbs function**, $\Delta G$, also known as the Gibbs free energy. For a spontaneous reaction, the Gibbs function is negative, and is related to the enthalpy and entropy changes for a reaction by the expression:

$$\Delta G = \Delta H - T\Delta S$$

  where $T$ is the absolute temperature at which the reaction occurs.
- An endothermic reaction will be spontaneous if the value of $\Delta S$ is such that $T\Delta S$ is larger than $\Delta H$.
- Exothermic reactions (the commonest) are generally spontaneous, since the negative value of $\Delta H$ usually dominates $T\Delta S$, making $\Delta G$ negative.
- Remember that spontaneous reactions may be unobservably slow if the activation energy for the reaction is high. Spontaneity is not an idea in chemical kinetics.

## Hess's law

Hess's law states that the enthalpy change for the process A $\longrightarrow$ B is independent of the route used to bring about the change.

This means that enthalpy changes can be found using other data. For example, enthalpies of reaction can be found from enthalpies of formation or enthalpies of combustion. It is possible, using Hess's law, to find the enthalpy change for reactions that cannot be performed directly.

### Using enthalpies of formation

The Hess's law diagram for using enthalpies of formation is shown below.

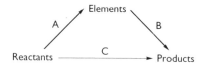

Hess's law says that C = A + B, where A, B and C are the enthalpy changes. Using the definition of enthalpies of formation:

A = −(sum of the enthalpies of formation of the reactants)

B = (sum of the enthalpies of formation of the products)

Therefore,

C = (sum of the enthalpies of formation of the products) − (sum of the enthalpies of formation of the reactants)

Consider the combustion of ethanol.

$$CH_3CH_2OH(l) + 3O_2(g) \longrightarrow 2CO_2(g) + 3H_2O(l)$$

The example shows how the heat change for the combustion of ethanol can be found. The states of all substances must be shown, because changes of state also involve enthalpy changes.

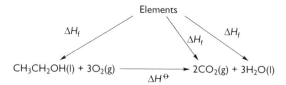

$$\Delta H^{\ominus} = 2\Delta H^{\ominus}_f(CO_2) + 3\Delta H^{\ominus}_f(H_2O) - \Delta H^{\ominus}_f(ethanol)$$

Inserting the appropriate values gives:

$$\Delta H^{\ominus} = 2(-393.5) + 3(-285.8) - (-277.1) = -1367.3 \text{ kJ mol}^{-1}$$

Note that oxygen is not included — it is an element in its standard state.

## Using enthalpies of combustion

The Hess's law diagram for using enthalpies of combustion is shown below.

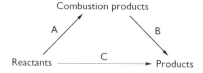

A = (sum of the enthalpies of combustion of the reactants)

B = −(sum of the enthalpies of combustion of the products)

Therefore:

C = (sum of the enthalpies of combustion of the reactants) − (sum of the enthalpies of combustion of the products)

Consider the reaction between ethanol and ethanoic acid, to give ethyl ethanoate and water:

$$CH_3CH_2OH(l) + CH_3COOH(l) \longrightarrow CH_3COOCH_2CH_3(l) + H_2O(l)$$

The Hess's law diagram for this reaction, using enthalpies of combustion, is shown below.

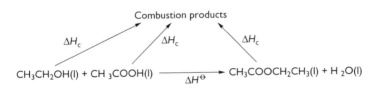

$$\Delta H^\ominus = \Delta H^\ominus_c(CH_3CH_2OH(l)) + \Delta H^\ominus_c(CH_3COOH(l)) - \Delta H^\ominus_c(CH_3COOCH_2CH_3(l))$$

Water, of course, does not burn! Inserting the appropriate values gives:

$$\Delta H^\ominus = (-1367.3) + (-874.1) - (-2237.9) = -3.5 \text{ kJ mol}^{-1}$$

# Measurement of enthalpy change

There are several simple experiments that can be used to measure enthalpy change. The following account is not intended to substitute for worksheets or other practical instructions. For details, you should consult a book of practical chemistry. The principles are as follows:

- use of a known amount of substance
- insulation against heat loss (although, since the temperature rise or fall for most reactions in solution is fairly small, heat loss is much less than is commonly imagined). The same is not true for combustion reactions (for instance, the burning of alcohols to find the heat of combustion), where the heat losses are colossal.
- correction of the maximum observed temperature change for heat loss or for slowness of reaction — this being particularly important for reactions between solids and liquids (e.g. heat of displacement in the reaction between copper(II) sulphate solution and zinc metal)
- calculation of the results

## Determination of enthalpy of neutralisation

This is a practical example for enthalpy change measurement.

- A known volume of acid of known concentration is placed in a polystyrene cup.
- The temperature of the acid is measured for 4 minutes.
- On the fifth minute, a known volume of a solution of a base of suitable concentration is added.
- The temperature is measured every 30 seconds until minute 8.
- A graph of temperature against time is plotted, and the lines extrapolated to enable the temperature change, $\Delta\theta$, at minute 5, corrected for any heat losses, to be calculated.

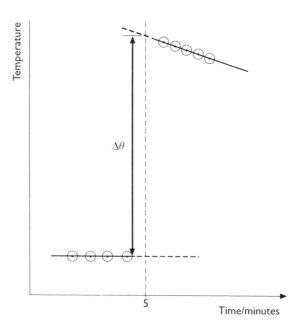

- The heat change is $mc\Delta\theta$, where $m$ is the mass of the solution (usually taken to be equal to its volume for aqueous solutions), $c$ is the heat capacity of the solution (usually taken to be equal to that of water for dilute aqueous solutions) and $\Delta\theta$ is the corrected temperature change.
- The heat change per mole of water formed is then found by dividing the result by the amount (number of moles) of hydrogen ions used.

### Use of mean bond enthalpies

Hess's law can be used to find approximate values of $\Delta H^{\ominus}$ for a reaction by use of mean bond enthalpies. The **mean bond enthalpy** is the enthalpy change when one mole of the specified type of bond is broken; an average value is taken which has been determined over a wide variety of molecules. This is the reason why it is approximate — bond enthalpies can vary quite a lot. Thus, the C=O bond enthalpy in $CO_2$ is 805 kJ mol$^{-1}$ but in methanal, HCHO, it is 695 k mol$^{-1}$. Breaking all the bonds in all the reactants leads to a collection of atoms; thus, polyatomic elements such as oxygen have to be included in the calculations, unlike in the case of enthalpies of formation.

The Hess's law diagram for the use of bond enthalpies is shown below.

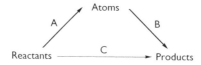

A = (sum of the bond enthalpies of the reactants)
B = -(sum of the bond enthalpies of the products)

Therefore:

C = (sum of the bond enthalpies of the reactants) – (sum of the bond enthalpies of the products)

Bond enthalpies are always endothermic, i.e. positive.

When working out enthalpies of reaction from bond enthalpies, use these rules:
- Write the reaction using structural formulae, so that you remember all the bonds.
- Ignore groups that are unchanged between the reactants and the products. In the esterification reaction already quoted, there is no need to involve the $CH_3CH_2-$ group, since it survives unchanged. There is no point in breaking all the bonds only to make them again.

Consider, again, the combustion of ethanol.

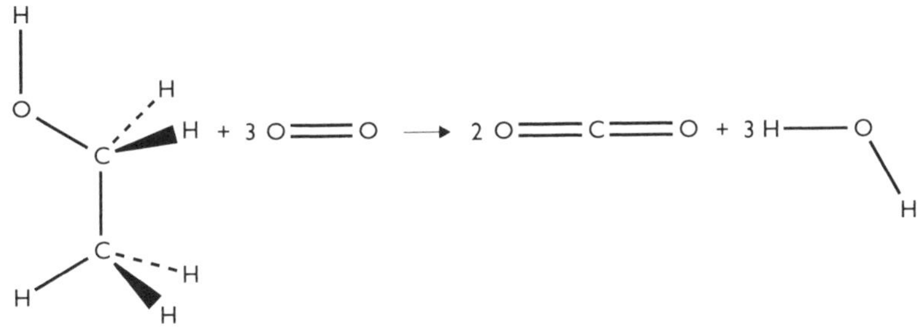

The bonds broken are 5 C–H, 1 C–C, 1 C–O (note the single bond) and 1 O–H. Those made are 4 C=O (note the double bond) and 6 O–H. Using the notation $E(X–X)$ to indicate the average bond enthalpy of the X–X bond and using the equation presented earlier, together with the bond enthalpies from the Data Book, the approximate enthalpy of reaction can be calculated:

approximate enthalpy of reaction
$$= [5E(C–H) + E(C–C) + E(C–O) + E(O–H)] – [4E(C=O) + 6E(O–H)]$$
$$= [(5 \times 413) + 347 + 358 + 464] – [(4 \times 805) + (6 \times 464)] \text{ kJ mol}^{-1}$$
$$= -2770 \text{ kJ mol}^{-1}$$

# Organic chemistry

## Introduction

### Homologous series

Organic chemistry is dominated by many varieties of **homologous series**. A homologous series is a series of compounds that:
- have a common general formula
- differ by $CH_2$

- show a trend in physical properties, for example boiling temperature
- show similar chemical properties, since all members of the same homologous series have the same **functional group**

The first member of a homologous series often shows differences in the detail of its chemistry from the succeeding members of the series.

The **alkenes** are an example of a homologous series in that:
- their general formula is $C_nH_{2n}$ (though not all compounds with this general formula are alkenes)
- they have a C=C double bond (which other compounds with the same general formula do not have)
- there is no alkene with only one carbon atom since there could not then be a C=C bond

The first three straight-chain compounds in the series are ethene, $CH_2=CH_2$, propene $CH_3CH=CH_2$, and butene. Butene has structural and geometric isomers (see below), but one version is but-1-ene, $CH_2=CHCH_2CH_3$. The boiling temperatures of these three alkenes are (in °C) –104, –47.7 and –6.2. All three react rapidly with bromine water, with potassium manganate(VII) solution, and all the other reagents given in the section on 'Reactions of alkenes' (p. 27).

A **functional group** is a small group of atoms or perhaps a single atom that determines the chemistry of a molecule. The homologous series and functional groups appropriate to AS are given in the table below. R represents an organic group.

| Series | General formula | First member |
|---|---|---|
| Alkanes | $C_nH_{2n+2}$ | $CH_4$, methane |
| Alkenes | $C_nH_{2n}$ | $CH_2=CH_2$, ethene |
| Halogenoalkanes | RX, where X is –Cl, –Br or –I | $CH_3Cl$, chloromethane (or bromo- or iodo-) |
| Primary alcohols | $RCH_2OH$ | $CH_3OH$, methanol |
| Secondary alcohols | where R and R' may be the same | $CH_3CH(OH)CH_3$, propan-2-ol |
| Tertiary alcohols | where R, R' and R" may be the same | $(CH_3)_3COH$, 2-methylpropan-2-ol |

The extra functional groups you will meet at A2 are shown below.

| Series | General formula | First member |
|---|---|---|
| Aldehydes | R**CHO** 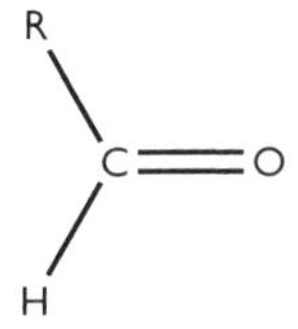 | HCHO, methanal |
| Ketones | 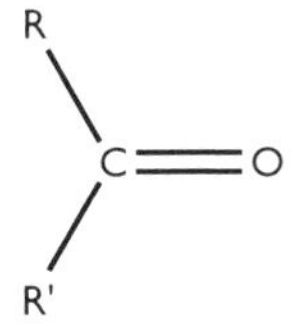 R**COR'** where R and R' may be the same | $CH_3COCH_3$, propanone |
| Carboxylic acids | R**COOH** 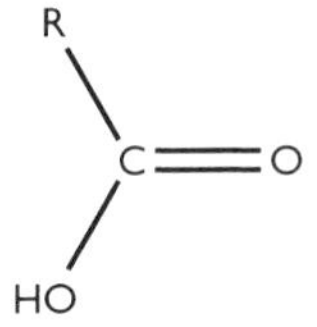 | HCOOH, methanoic acid |
| Acid chlorides | R**COCl** 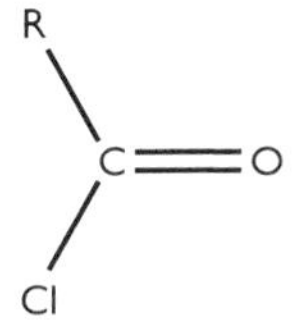 | $CH_3COCl$, ethanoyl chloride |
| Esters | R**COOR'** 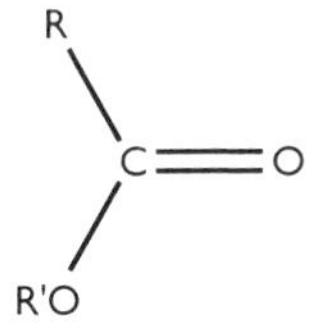 where R and R' may be the same, while R, but not R', may be H | $HCOOCH_3$, methyl methanoate |
| Primary amines | R**NH₂** | $CH_3NH_2$, aminomethane |
| Nitriles | R**CN** | $CH_3CN$, ethanonitrile |
| Amides | R**CONH₂** 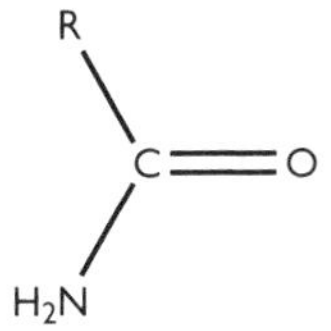 | $CH_3CONH_2$, ethanamide |

| Series | General formula | First member |
|---|---|---|
| Amino acids | 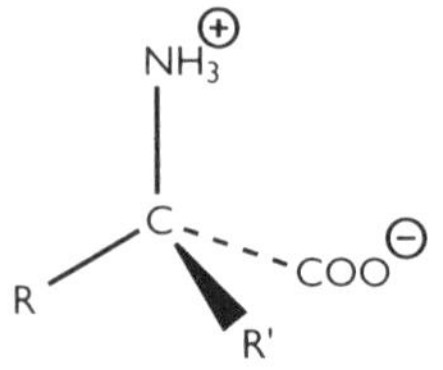 where R and R' may be the same or different, or may be H (as in glycine) | $^-OOCCH_2NH_3^+$, glycine (this form is called a zwitterion, where the acidic COOH group has given its proton to the basic $NH_2$ group) |

## Systematic names

The International Union of Pure and Applied Chemistry (IUPAC) has generated a series of rules giving organic compounds **systematic names**. Knowing the rules and the systematic name of a compound means the formula can be written, and vice versa.

The names may be very long if the compounds are large. Systematic names are used in the Edexcel specification for most organic substances, though there are exceptions, for example the amino acid glycine. However, systematic names are less common in chemistry beyond school level. Partly this is because American textbooks and chemical suppliers do not often use them. Also, the names are unwieldy if more than five or six carbon atoms are involved — the vitamin folic acid has a systematic name some three lines long!

The use of molecular models in learning nomenclature, as well as isomerism and stereochemistry, is a course I recommend. Molecular model kits are quite cheap and will transform your understanding of structure.

### Rules for systematic names
- Identify the longest carbon chain — take care with this, since structures can be written with 90° bond angles that can mask the longest chain. The compound below has a 4-carbon, not 3-carbon, longest chain.

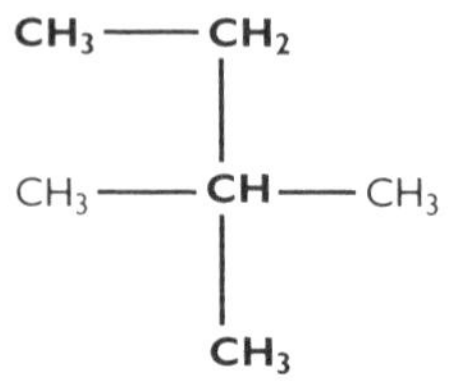

$$CH_3 - CH_2$$
$$|$$
$$CH_3 - CH - CH_3$$
$$|$$
$$CH_3$$

- The name is based on the alkane with the same number of carbon atoms as the longest chain.
- Substituent groups have the name ending changed to -yl. This is illustrated for alkanes up to $C_5$ in the table below.

| C | Alkane | Name stem | Substituent group | Structure |
|---|--------|-----------|-------------------|-----------|
| 1 | Methane $CH_4$ | Meth- | Methyl | $CH_3-$ |
| 2 | Ethane $C_2H_6$ | Eth- | Ethyl | $CH_3CH_2-$ |
| 3 | Propane $C_3H_8$ | Prop- | Propyl | $CH_3CH_2CH_2-$ |
| 4 | Butane $C_4H_{10}$ | But- | Butyl | $CH_3CH_2CH_2CH_2-$ |
| 5 | Pentane $C_5H_{12}$ | Pent- | Pentyl | $CH_3CH_2CH_2CH_2CH_2-$ |

- The position of each substituent group is indicated by a number. This corresponds to the position in the chain of the carbon atom to which it is attached, so that the number of the substituent group is the lowest possible. However, for substances such as carboxylic acids, RCOOH, where the functional group is at the end of a chain, the carbon atoms are always numbered from that end.
- Different series of compounds have the name ending modified to indicate which homologous series is involved.
- Where two groups that are the same are substituted on a given carbon atom, the number is repeated and the substituent is prefixed 'di'.
- Where two groups that are the same are on different carbons, 'di' is still used; if there are three groups on the same or different carbons, then 'tri' is used; if there are four groups then 'tetra' is used, and so on.

## Examples of systematic names
*Alkanes*

$$CH_3$$
$$|$$
$$CH_3CH_2CHCH_3$$

2-methylbutane

$$CH_3 \quad CH_3$$
$$| \qquad |$$
$$CH_3CCH_2CHCH_3$$
$$|$$
$$CH_3$$

2,2,4-trimethylpentane

*Alkenes*
The position of the double bond (or bonds) is given by the number of the carbon atom where the double bond starts.

$CH_3CH=CH_2$
Propene

$CH_3CH_2CH=CH_2$
But-1-ene

$CH_3CH=CHCH_3$
But-2-ene

$CH_2=CH-CH=CH_3$
Buta-1,3-diene; not an alkene, but an alkadiene

*Halogenoalkanes*

$CH_3CH_2CH_2Cl$
1-chloropropane

$BrCH_2CH_2Br$
1,2-dibromoethane

$CH_3CHCH_3$
$|$
Br
2-bromopropane

*Alcohols*

$$CH_3CH_2CH_2OH$$
Propan-1-ol

$$HOCH_2CH_2OH$$
Ethan-1,2-diol

$$CH_3CHCH_3$$
$$|$$
$$OH$$
Propan-2-ol

*Aldehydes*

$$CH_3CH_2CH_2CHO$$
Butanal

$$CH_3$$
$$|$$
$$CH_3CHCH_2CH_2CHO$$
4-methylpentanal

*Ketones*

$$CH_3COCH_3$$
Propanone

$$CH_3COCH_2CH_2CH_3$$
Pentan-2-one

$$CH_3CH_2COCH_2CH_3$$
Pentan-3-one

*Carboxylic acids*

$$CCH_3CH_2CH_2COOH$$
Butanoic acid

$$CH_3CH=CH_2COOH$$
But-2-enoic acid

$$CH_3CHCH_2COOH$$
$$|$$
$$OH$$
3-hydroxybutanoic acid

$$CH_2=CHCOOH$$
Propenoic acid

$$CH_3CH_2COOH$$
Propanoic acid — note the difference

$$HOOC–COOH$$
Ethanedioic acid

# Isomerism

## Structural isomerism

- Structural isomers are compounds that have the same molecular formula but different structural formulae.
- The compounds can be of the same type. Thus, propan-1-ol and propan-2-ol are structural isomers, as are pentan-2-one and pentan-3-one.
- The compounds may be of different types. Thus, the molecular formula $C_2H_6O$ could represent ethanol, $CH_3CH_2OH$, or the totally different methoxymethane, $CH_3OCH_3$, which is an ether. Sometimes this is called functional group isomerism.
- The number of structural isomers rises rapidly with the number of carbon atoms in the compound. This is shown in the table below, using alkanes, $C_nH_{2n+2}$, as examples.

| Alkane | Number of isomers |
|--------|-------------------|
| $C_8H_{18}$ | 18 |
| $C_{10}H_{22}$ | 75 |
| $C_{12}H_{26}$ | 355 |
| $C_{14}H_{30}$ | 1858 |
| $C_{20}H_{42}$ | 366 319 |
| $C_{25}H_{52}$ | 36 797 588 |
| $C_{30}H_{62}$ | 4 111 846 763 |
| $C_{40}H_{82}$ | 62 491 178 805 831 |

Because the number of structures can be large, even for small compounds, always use the structural formula to eliminate ambiguity.

### Geometric (*cis-trans*) isomerism

Geometric (*cis-trans*) isomerism results from restricted rotation about a carbon–carbon double bond, provided that the groups on a given carbon in the C=C bond are not the same.

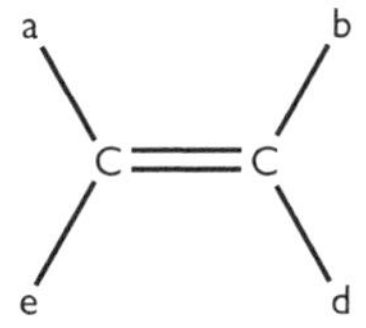

Thus, in the diagram above, 'a' and 'e' must be different, as must 'b' and 'd'. The groups do not all have to be different from one another. The diagram below shows two geometric isomers.

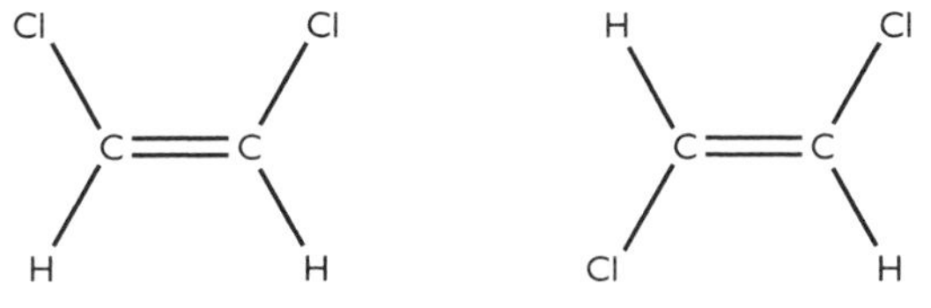

These are *cis-* and *trans-*1,2-dichloroethene. In *cis-* isomers, the substituent groups, in this case the same, are on the same side of the C=C bond.

Geometric isomers can also arise in ring compounds.

## Classification of reactions

Reactions are classified in terms of their reaction mechanism. The classifications for reagents and reactions are given here; the mechanisms themselves do not appear until Unit 5.

| Type of reagent | Definition | Examples |
|---|---|---|
| Free radical | An atom or molecule having an unpaired electron, indicated by • | •Cl, •Br |
| Electrophile | A species that seeks areas of negative charge in the molecule it is attacking; it may have a positive charge or have one induced during the reaction | $Br_2$ (attacking ethene), $NO_2^+$, $CH_3CO^+$ |
| Nucleophile | A species having a lone pair of electrons which attack areas of positive charge on other molecules | $Cl^-$, $Br^-$, $I^-$, $OH^-$, $NH_3$, $H_2O$, $RNH_2$ |

| Type of reaction | Reaction examples |
|---|---|
| Free radical | Alkanes with halogens; polymerisation of alkenes |
| Electrophilic addition | Alkenes with bromine or hydrogen halides |
| Nucleophilic substitution | Halogenoalkanes with aqueous hydroxide ions to give alcohols; with cyanide ions to give nitriles; with ammonia to give amines |
| Elimination | Halogenoalkanes with hydroxide ions in ethanolic solution to give alkenes |
| Hydrolysis | Halogenoalkanes with water or with aqueous sodium hydroxide |
| Reduction | Alkenes with hydrogen |
| Oxidation | Alcohols with potassium dichromate(VI) in sulphuric acid |
| Polymerisation | Alkenes to give poly(alkenes) |

# Reactions of organic compounds

## Reactions of alkanes

### Reaction with oxygen

In a plentiful supply of oxygen or air, alkanes burn on ignition to form carbon dioxide and water. The reactions are strongly exothermic.

- Methane is present in natural gas.

$$CH_4 + 2O_2 \longrightarrow CO_2 + 2H_2O$$

- Petrol is a mixture that can be represented by octane.

$$C_8H_{18} + 12\tfrac{1}{2}O_2 \longrightarrow 8CO_2 + 9H_2O$$

In internal combustion engines, complete combustion does not occur; carbon and carbon monoxide are produced as well as carbon dioxide. In limited oxygen, all of the hydrogen in a given molecule is always oxidised — hydrogen is never a product.

### Reaction with chlorine or bromine

In the presence of UV light, alkanes react with chlorine or bromine to produce halogenoalkanes. In strong UV or focused sunlight, the reaction is explosive.

The reaction involves radical substitution. There is a mixture of products, because radicals (in this case halogen atoms) are very reactive and reactions with the first halogenoalkane produced occur, resulting in further substitution. Methane reacting with chlorine gives $CH_3Cl$ initially; this reacts to give, successively, $CH_2Cl_2$, $CHCl_3$ and $CCl_4$. Direct halogenation is not a good way of making single compounds, but is useful for making solvents, which can be mixtures.

$$CH_4 + Cl_2 \longrightarrow CH_3Cl + HCl$$
$$CH_4 + Br_2 \longrightarrow CH_3Br + HBr$$

## Reactions of alkenes

Propene, $CH_3CH=CH_2$, is a good example because it is an unsymmetrical alkene, i.e. the substituents on each end of the C=C bond are not the same. This is significant in some reactions.

### Reaction with hydrogen

Propene reacts with hydrogen at room temperature in the presence of a platinum catalyst, or at 150 °C with a nickel catalyst, to give propane.

$$CH_3CH=CH_2 + H_2 \longrightarrow CH_3CH_2CH_3$$

This particular reaction is not industrially useful — alkenes are far more valuable than alkanes, since they are more reactive. However, it is the basis of margarine manufacture, while the reduction of C=C bonds in more complex molecules is often required.

### Reaction with halogens

Propene reacts with chlorine or bromine in the gas phase, or in an inert solvent (e.g. $CCl_4$), at room temperature.

$$CH_3CH=CH_2 + Br_2 \longrightarrow CH_3CHBrCH_2Br$$

The product is 1,2-dibromopropane. The brown bromine is decolorised. This reaction is the basis for the test for alkenes, using bromine water.

### Reaction with hydrogen halides

Propene reacts with hydrogen bromide in the gas phase or in an inert solvent at room temperature.

$$CH_3CH=CH_2 + HBr \longrightarrow CH_3CHBrCH_3$$

The major product is 2-bromopropane (shown above) with some 1-bromopropane. The reaction is an electrophilic addition.

The hydrogen goes to the carbon atom in the double bond that already has most hydrogen atoms on it. This is Markovnikoff's rule; this 'rule' is not an *explanation* and there are some exceptions to it. It is no more than a useful guide. (The reasons for the orientation of the addition are dealt with in Unit 5.) Hydrogen chloride and hydrogen iodide react similarly to hydrogen bromide.

### Reaction with potassium manganate(VII) solution

Propene reacts with potassium manganate(VII) solution, $KMnO_4$, whether it is acidic (in $H_2SO_4$), neutral or alkaline (in $Na_2CO_3$), to give propan-1,2-diol.

$$CH_3CH=CH_2 \xrightarrow{KMnO_4} CH_3CH(OH)CH_2OH$$

The precise nature of this reaction is still not known, so a balanced equation is not written. The purple $KMnO_4$ solution is usually converted to a brown sludge of $MnO_2$.

## Reactions of halogenoalkanes

The reactions are similar whether chloro-, bromo- or iodo- compounds are involved. The rates of reaction are in the order Cl < Br < I.

### Reaction with potassium hydroxide in aqueous solution

Halogenoalkanes heated under reflux with aqueous KOH (or NaOH) give mainly the alcohol in a nucleophilic substitution reaction.

$$CH_3CH_2CH_2CH_2Br + KOH \longrightarrow CH_3CH_2CH_2CH_2OH + KBr$$

Some ethanol is often added to improve the miscibility of the reagents. There is always some elimination (see below) at the same time.

### Reaction with potassium hydroxide in ethanolic solution

With ethanolic KOH, halogenoalkanes eliminate HX to give an alkene. There is always some substitution at the same time.

$$CH_3CH_2CH_2CH_2Br + KOH \longrightarrow CH_3CH_2CH=CH_2 + KBr + H_2O$$

### Reaction with potassium cyanide in ethanolic solution

Halogenoalkanes heated under reflux with KCN in ethanol give nitriles, RCN, in a nucleophilic substitution reaction.

$$CH_3CH_2CH_2CH_2Br + KCN \longrightarrow CH_3CH_2CH_2CH_2CN + KBr$$

This is one of the few reactions where C–C bonds can be made.

### Reaction with ammonia

Halogenoalkanes heated in a sealed tube with concentrated ammonia give a mixture of amines. The primary amine, $RNH_2$, can be made the major product by using excess ammonia. The reaction is a nucleophilic substitution.

$$CH_3CH_2CH_2CH_2Br + 2NH_3 \longrightarrow CH_3CH_2CH_2CH_2NH_2 + NH_4Br$$

A mixture is given because the amine produced is also a nucleophile and attacks any unchanged halogenoalkane.

### Identifying the halogen atom in a halogenoalkane

- Heat the halogenoalkane with sodium hydroxide solution to hydrolyse it to the alcohol and sodium halide.

$$CH_3Br + NaOH \longrightarrow CH_3OH + Na^+ + Br^-$$

- Acidify the solution with nitric acid (test with litmus).

- Add silver nitrate solution.

A white precipitate soluble in dilute ammonia indicates chloride; a cream precipitate soluble in concentrated ammonia indicates bromide; a yellow precipitate insoluble in ammonia indicates iodide.

Apart from the initial hydrolysis, these reactions are the standard tests for halide ions.

# The reactions of primary, secondary and tertiary alcohols

### Reaction with acidified potassium dichromate(VI)

Generally, balanced equations are not written for these reactions. The oxidising agent, which is potassium dichromate(VI) and dilute sulphuric acid, is represented by [O].

**Primary alcohols** react initially to give an aldehyde which, if not removed from the reaction system, oxidises further to give a carboxylic acid.

$$CH_3CH_2OH + [O] \longrightarrow CH_3CHO + H_2O$$
$$CH_3CHO + [O] \longrightarrow CH_3COOH$$

The oxidising agent changes colour from orange to green.

**Secondary alcohols** react to give ketones. The ketones are not oxidised further under these conditions, so the mixture can be heated under reflux.

$$CH_3CH(OH)CH_3 + [O] \longrightarrow CH_3COCH_3 + H_2O$$

**Tertiary alcohols** do not react under these conditions.

### Reaction with dehydrating agents

Dehydrating agents remove water from alcohols to give alkenes. Tertiary alcohols dehydrate easily and heating alone is often enough. Primary and secondary alcohols are heated with concentrated sulphuric acid — some oxidation always occurs as well.

$$CH_3CH_2CH_2OH \longrightarrow CH_3CH=CH_2 + H_2O$$
$$CH_3CH(OH)CH_3 \longrightarrow CH_3CH=CH_2 + H_2O$$
$$(CH_3)_2C(OH)CH_3 \longrightarrow (CH_3)_2C=CH_2 + H_2O$$

### Reaction with halogenating agents

Alcohols can be converted into halogenoalkanes in several ways, which work for all three types of alcohol.

#### Using phosphorus pentachloride

Solid $PCl_5$ reacts readily with alcohols at room temperature to give the chloroalkane and HCl gas, emitted as steamy fumes.

$$CH_3CH_2OH + PCl_5 \longrightarrow CH_3CH_2Cl + HCl + POCl_3$$

#### Using a mixture of sodium bromide and 50% sulphuric acid

The alcohol is heated under reflux with the reagents. The method can be used for chlorides using NaCl, but not for iodides, since sulphuric acid oxidises iodides to iodine (Unit 1).

$$CH_3CH_2OH + NaBr + H_2SO_4 \longrightarrow CH_3CH_2Br + NaHSO_4 + H_2O$$

*Using a mixture of iodine and moist red phosphorus*

If alcohols are warmed with this mixture, iodoalkanes are formed. The first reaction is the production of phosphorus triiodide, which then reacts with the alcohol.

$$P_4 + 6I_2 \longrightarrow 4PI_3$$
$$3CH_3CH_2OH + PI_3 \longrightarrow 3CH_3CH_2I + H_3PO_3$$

### Test for the –OH group

The reaction with $PCl_5$ (above) can be used as a test for the –OH group. It is not specific to alcohols; the –OH groups in carboxylic acids give the same reaction but these acids would also affect indicators, which alcohols do not.

# Bonding and reactivity

The reactivity of organic compounds is related to:

- whether the compound is saturated or unsaturated
- the polarity of the attacked bond(s), since many reagents (nucleophiles, electrophiles) are charged or are polar themselves
- the bond enthalpy of any bond that must be broken

## Alkanes and alkenes: single vs double bonds

- Alkanes are saturated, so the bonds must be broken before substitution can occur.
- Alkanes are not polar.
- Alkene C=C bonds have one σ-bond and one π-bond; the latter has accessible electron density that can be attacked by electrophiles.

The result is that the conditions under which alkanes react are more severe than those for alkenes — compare the reactions of these compounds with bromine.

## Bond polarity

- A polar bond is more susceptible to attack by an electrophile or a nucleophile than is a non-polar bond.
- The greater the polarity, the greater is the reactivity.
- However, polarity considerations may come second to those of bond enthalpy (see 'Bond enthalpy', below).

The result is that increasing the polarity of a given bond increases its reactivity — thus, chloroethane, $CH_3CH_2Cl$, reacts slowly with water at room temperature but ethanoyl chloride, $CH_3COCl$, reacts dangerously quickly. The C=O next to the chlorine makes the C–Cl bond much more polar, i.e. the carbon atom is more δ+ and so it reacts with nucleophilic water much more quickly.

In the case of alkanes, the C–H bonds are not polar, so they are not attacked by either electrophiles or nucleophiles. They are attacked instead by free radicals which are extremely reactive.

Alcohols are subject to nucleophilic attack, since the C–O bond is polar and so the carbon atom is δ+.

## Bond enthalpy

A high bond enthalpy means that the bond is hard to break. Therefore, the activation energy for the reaction will be high and so the reaction will be slow. The effect is seen particularly in the reactivity of halogenoalkanes towards hydroxide ions or other nucleophiles; thus, the rates for ethyl compounds are $C_2H_5Cl < C_2H_5Br < C_2H_5I$.

This is the opposite to what would be expected from bond polarities, the C–Cl bond being the most polar. However, it parallels the bond enthalpies ($kJ\,mol^{-1}$): C–Cl, 338; C–Br, 276; C–I, 238. The weaker the bond, the faster is the reaction.

The inertness of PTFE (see page 36) is due to the high C–F bond strength at $484\,kJ\,mol^{-1}$.

# Quantitative chemistry related to this topic

## Empirical and molecular formulae

The empirical formula is the formula of a compound in its lowest terms. Therefore, $CH_2$ is the empirical formula of any compound $C_nH_{2n}$, i.e. all alkenes, cycloalkanes and poly(alkenes). The calculation steps give:
- the number of moles of each atom
- the ratio of moles of atoms

To find the molecular formula, you need additional information, such as the molar mass of the compound.

### Example 1
Sodium burns in oxygen to give an oxide containing 58.97% sodium. What is the empirical formula of this substance?

*Answer*
Since the compound is an oxide of sodium, there must be 41.03% oxygen in it.

The three steps needed to calculate the empirical formula are given in the table headings.

| | Divide by r.a.m. | Divide by smallest | Ratio of atoms |
|---|---|---|---|
| Sodium | 58.97/23 = 2.564 | 2.564/2.564 = 1 | 1 |
| Oxygen | 41.03/16 = 2.564 | 2.564/2.564 = 1 | 1 |

The compound has an empirical formula of NaO. This is the simplest or lowest ratio of the atoms. The compound is actually sodium peroxide, $Na_2O_2$, and is not strictly an oxide. In true oxides, the oxidation state of the oxygen is $-2$; in peroxides it is $-1$.

## Example 2

A compound contains 73.47% carbon, 10.20% hydrogen and the remainder is oxygen. The relative molecular mass is 98; find the empirical and molecular formulae of the compound.

*Answer*

|  | Divide by r.a.m. | Divide by smallest | Ratio of atoms |
|---|---|---|---|
| Carbon | 73.47/12 = 6.1225 | 6.1225/1.020 = 6 | 6 |
| Hydrogen | 10.20/1 = 10.20 | 10.20/1.020 = 10 | 10 |
| Oxygen | 16.33/16 = 1.020 | 1.020/1.020 = 1 | 1 |

The compound has the empirical formula $C_6H_{10}O$. Its mass is
$$(6 \times 12) + (10 \times 1) + 16 = 98$$
So the empirical formula is also the molecular formula.

## Example 3

This example shows why *you must not do any rounding* during the calculation.

A compound contains 39.13% carbon, 52.17% oxygen and 8.70% hydrogen. Calculate the empirical formula.

*Answer*

|  | Divide by r.a.m. | Divide by smallest | Ratio of atoms |
|---|---|---|---|
| Carbon | 39.13/12 = 3.26 | 3.26/3.26 = 1 | 1 |
| Oxygen | 52.17/16 = 3.26 | 3.26/3.26 = 1 | 1 |
| Hydrogen | 8.70/1 = 8.70 | 8.70/3.26 = 2.66 | 2.66 |

The ratios are not whole numbers. This means you have to multiply by a small integer, usually 2 or 3, to get the answer. In this case, multiplying by three gives 3, 3, 8, so the empirical formula is $C_3H_8O_3$.

# Theoretical and percentage yields

The calculation of theoretical yield and percentage yield in organic reactions is simply an extension of the ideas of reacting masses. The yield is never 100% because:
- organic reactions seldom occur by one route or give a single product — for example, the reaction of propene with HBr
- there are always handling losses — distillation in Quickfit apparatus will lose some product due to the wetting of the joints, and filtration of a solid leaves quite a significant amount that cannot be retrieved from the filter paper

A yield of 80% would be considered quite good. Two such reactions, one after the other, would give 64% overall; three would give only 51%. This is why synthetic routes (Unit 5) use as few steps as possible.

## Example 1

In the reaction shown below, 4.6 g of ethanol gave 8.5 g of bromoethane. Find the theoretical and percentage yields.

$$C_2H_5OH + KBr + H_2SO_4 \longrightarrow C_2H_5Br + KHSO_4 + H_2O$$

### Answer

The molar masses of the relevant compounds are needed: ethanol 46, bromoethane 109, both g mol$^{-1}$.

$$\text{Amount (moles) of ethanol} = \frac{4.6\,g}{46\,g\,mol^{-1}} = 0.10\,mol$$

Amount of bromoethane for 100% yield = 0.10 mol

Mass of bromoethane = 0.10 mol × 109 g mol$^{-1}$ = 10.9 g

$$\text{Percentage yield} = \frac{8.5\,g \times 100}{10.9\,g} = 78\%$$

Given that the data come from an experiment where there will be handling losses, quoting the percentage yield to more than two significant figures is self-delusion.

## Example 2

In an experiment to make ethyl ethanoate by the reaction

$$C_2H_5OH + CH_3COOH \longrightarrow CH_3COOC_2H_5 + H_2O$$

20.2 g of ethanol was heated under reflux with 35.0 g of ethanoic acid. 15 g of ethyl ethanoate was obtained. Find the theoretical and percentage yield of ethyl ethanoate.

### Answer

Where the masses of both substances are given, it is possible that one of them is in excess over the other. The one that is present in the least amount limits the amount of product that can form — it is the controlling reagent.

Molar masses/g mol$^{-1}$: ethanol 46, ethanoic acid 60, ethyl ethanoate 88.

$$\text{Amount of ethanol} = \frac{20.2\,g}{46\,g\,mol^{-1}} = 0.44\,mol$$

$$\text{Amount of ethanoic acid} = \frac{35.0\,g}{60\,g\,mol^{-1}} = 0.58\,mol$$

The ethanoic acid is thus in excess, and the yield will depend on the amount of ethanol. The amount of ethyl ethanoate obtained could not be more than 0.44 mol.

Theoretical yield = 0.44 mol × 88 g mol$^{-1}$ = 38.7 g

$$\text{Percentage yield} = \frac{15.0\,g \times 100}{38.7\,g} = 38.8\% \text{ or } 39\% \text{ to 2 significant figures}$$

The yield in this reaction will never approach the theoretical yield, since the reaction is an equilibrium, more properly represented as follows:

$$C_2H_5OH + CH_3COOH \rightleftharpoons CH_3COOC_2H_5 + H_2O$$

# Applied organic chemistry

## Liquid and gaseous fuels

The advantages and disadvantages of liquid and gaseous fuels depend on:
- whether the fuel has to be carried with the device using it (as in motor vehicles) or if it can be piped (as in domestic gas supplies)
- any safety aspects peculiar to the particular fuel, especially the handling of potentially explosive gases (these do not include flammability, which some exam candidates seem to think is a problem — non-flammable fuels are rare)
- the energy yield per unit volume or unit mass

| Fuel | $M_r$ | $\Delta H_c$/kJ mol$^{-1}$ | $\Delta H_c$/kJ cm$^{-3}$ | $\Delta H_c$/kJ g$^{-1}$ |
|---|---|---|---|---|
| Hydrogen(g) | 2 | −286 | −0.012 | −143 |
| Methane(g) | 16 | −890 | −0.037 | −55.6 |
| Butane(g) | 58 | −2877 | −0.12 | −49.6 |
| Butane(l) | 58 | −2877 | −29.8 | −49.6 |
| Octane(l) | 114 | −5470 | −33.8 | −48 |
| Ethanol(l) | 46 | −1367 | −23.4 | −29.7 |

(The molar volume of the gases is taken as 24 dm$^3$.)

### Hydrogen and methane

Hydrogen and methane have a high energy yield per gram, but are not very dense and therefore large volumes of gas are needed. They are used where the fuel can be piped to the point of use.

Hydrogen can be used in cars — it is compressed and adsorbed in a suitable metal sponge. However, the range of such vehicles is limited and the relatively heavy gas canisters take up a lot of space. There are presently no widespread hydrogen filling stations.

All gaseous fuels present special handling requirements to avoid leakage of flammable or explosive gases. However, these problems have been solved.

### *Environmental factors*

Hydrogen burns to water only. Remember, though, that the means of producing hydrogen (electrolysis of brine or reaction of methane with steam) consumes energy, so the environmental advantages in one place have costs elsewhere. Methane is used in fixed systems and is burned efficiently, so that little carbon monoxide pollution results.

### Butane

Butane has a high energy yield per gram, but the gas is not very dense. It is easily liquefied by compression to give LPG. Butane can be used in cars adapted for it — the number of filling stations selling it is rising. It is also used in tanks and cylinders as a constituent of Calor gas. The liquid form vaporises readily and requires special handling facilities.

### Octane
Octane has a high energy yield per gram, and is the densest of the fuels listed. Therefore, manageable volumes of the fuel can be carried in motor vehicles. It is universally available. The liquid is volatile, but not so volatile that special handling is needed.

*Environmental factors*
The yield of carbon monoxide from internal combustion engines is quite high. Most of this can be removed by the use of catalytic converters in which CO reacts with the nitrogen oxides that are also produced, to give nitrogen and $CO_2$.

### Ethanol
Ethanol has a high energy yield per gram, but it is not as dense as octane. Therefore, larger volumes of liquid are needed than in the case of octane. It is made from oil if that is available, so it is not a cost-effective fuel for countries that have relatively cheap oil. Countries such as Brazil that have no oil but have a lot of sugar cane can make cheap, fuel-grade ethanol by fermentation; car fuel in Brazil contains 20% ethanol and 80% ordinary petrol.

*Environmental factors*
Ethanol is a clean fuel, producing little carbon monoxide.

## Structure and properties of polymers

### Structure of polymers
Alkenes form polymers in radical reactions. The only carbon atoms in the chain are those from the C=C bond; all the others are in the side-chains.

| Monomer | Polymer* |
|---|---|
| Ethene | Poly(ethene) |
| Propene | Poly(propene) |

| Monomer | Polymer* |
|---------|----------|
| Chloroethene 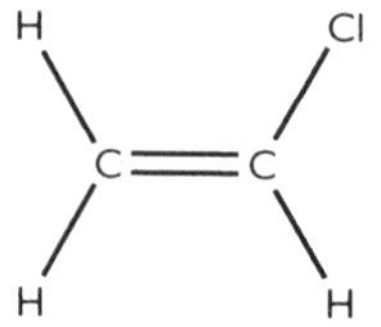 | Poly(chloroethene), PVC 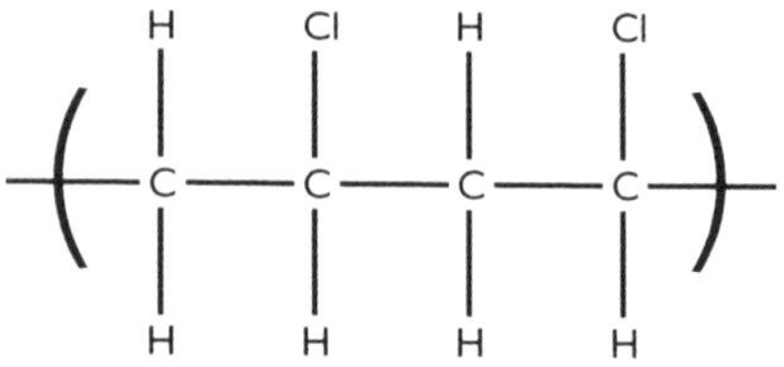 |
| Tetrafluoroethene 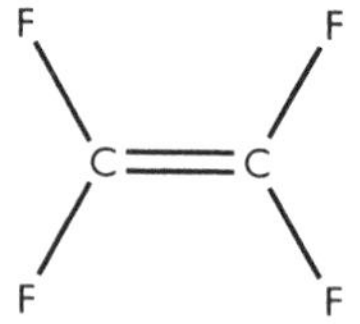 | Poly(tetrafluoroethene), PTFE 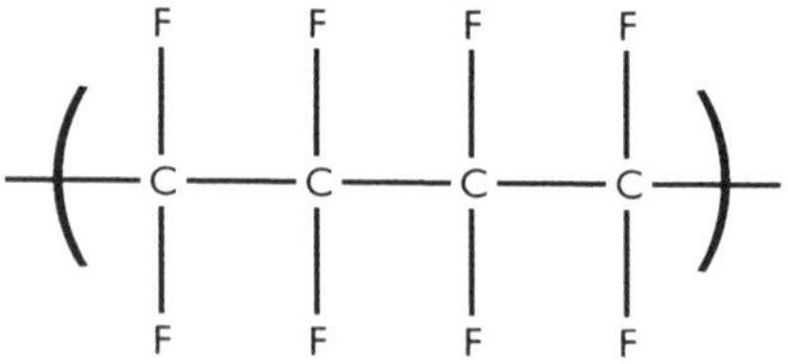 |

* In each case, the repeating unit is half of the polymer structure shown.

There are two varieties of poly(ethene), low- and high-density. High-density poly(ethene) (hdpe) has a regular structure that packs more densely than low-density poly(ethene) (ldpe). High-density poly(ethene) is made using a Ziegler-Natta catalyst which gives controlled polymerisation (and earned Ziegler and Natta a Nobel prize). It is harder and stiffer than low-density poly(ethene).

## Uses of polymers
**Poly(ethene) (ldpe):**
- packaging film and bags
- electrical insulation

**Poly(ethene) (hdpe):**
- water tanks and pipes
- polythene bottles
- household items, for example washing-up bowls and buckets

**Poly(propene):**
- ropes
- containers that have to be heat-sterilised or withstand boiling water

**Poly(chloroethene):**
- window frames, guttering, pipes
- flooring
- film wrap
- electrical insulation

**Poly(tetrafluoroethene) (PTFE):**
- non-stick coatings
- piping resistant to chemical attack
- electrical insulation
- low-friction, low-maintenance bearings, for example expansion bearings in bridges

PTFE is very expensive, and so its uses tend to be specialist, low-volume ones.

## Halogens, herbicides and polymers

Halogens are used in the manufacture of herbicides and polymers.

### Herbicides

Herbicides are designed to kill plants. The two shown below are selective weedkillers, affecting only dicotyledons (broad-leaved plants) and not grasses. They are chlorinated compounds.

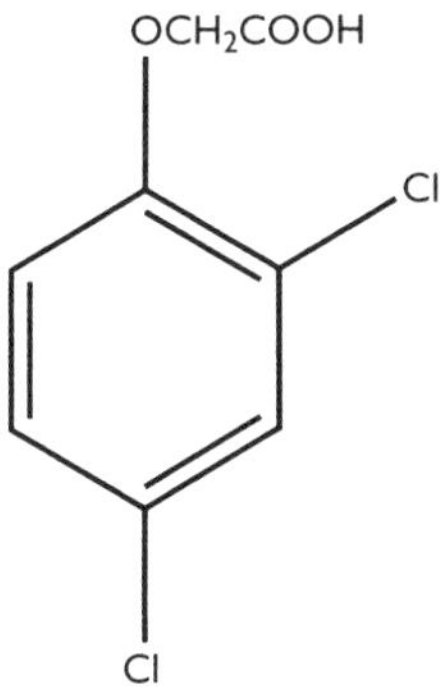

2,4-D 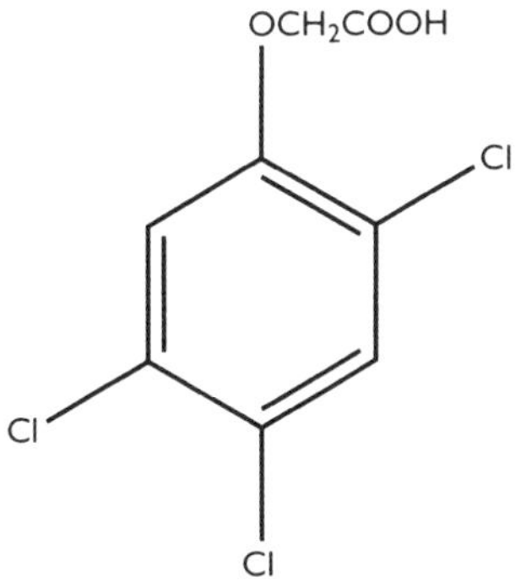                2,4,5-T

You are not expected to be able to recall these structures.

The effectiveness of the compounds depends on their not being readily hydrolysed in the environment. This is related to the strength of the C–Cl bonds, which are stronger in aromatic compounds like these than they are in chloroalkanes. The polluting effect of the compounds is also related to the strength of the C–Cl bonds. Since they are resistant to breakdown, excessive use can lead to contamination of soil and of water supplies.

### Halogenated polymers

The two commonest halogenated polymers are poly(chloroethene) and poly(tetrafluoroethene) (see above). Both are useful because they are resistant to hydrolytic attack, again because of the strength of the C–X bond. Both are therefore persistent in the environment, although, unlike weedkillers, they are not themselves toxic.

# Kinetics

The factors that control the rate of a chemical reaction include:
- the concentration of the reagents (for reactions in solution)
- the temperature of the reaction system
- the pressure (for reactions in the gas phase)

- the surface area of any solid reagents
- the presence of a catalyst

## Collision theory

Chemicals cannot react unless they collide. The theory of reaction rates is therefore called **collision theory**. When thinking about reaction rates, you should do so on a molecular level and try to imagine the collisions occurring.

The important factors are:
- the number of collisions per unit time — the **collision frequency**
- the energy with which the particles collide — the **collision energy**
- the **orientation** in which the particles collide — particularly important for large molecules

Only a very small proportion of the collisions that occur in a reaction system are successful, i.e. lead to the formation of products.

### Collision frequency

Collision frequency increases with concentration in a liquid system, or with an increase in pressure in a gaseous one. In each case, the distance between colliding species is reduced, so there is less distance to travel before encountering another molecule.

Collision frequency increases with surface area for a solid reagent. In this case, the increased area raises the probability of a molecule in the other phase (gas or liquid) colliding with the solid.

Collision frequency increases with temperature. The molecules are moving faster and so travel the necessary distance more quickly.

### Collision energy

The minimum collision energy needed for particles to react is called the **activation energy**, $E_a$. Particles that collide with an energy greater than $E_a$ will react if their orientation is correct.

Increasing the temperature increases the proportion of particles that collide with energies greater than $E_a$. The effect of an increase in temperature on collision energy is more important than the effect on collision frequency. The collision frequency rises roughly linearly with rising temperature, but the increase in the number of particles with collision energies above $E_a$ is exponential.

### Orientation

Particles must collide in such a way that the reactive parts of them come into contact.

## Maxwell–Boltzmann distribution of molecular energies

The graphs below show the distribution of energy between molecules in a gas at temperature $T_1$ and at a higher temperature $T_2$.

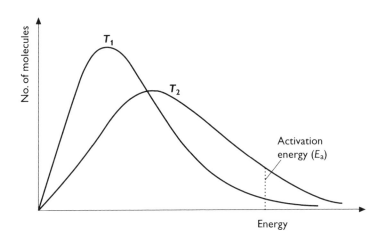

There are several points to note about the graphs.
- Both graphs start at the origin.
- The distribution is skewed.
- The graph does not meet the *x*-axis at high energies.
- The higher temperature graph has its peak at higher energy but the peak is lower than the graph for $T_1$. This is because the area under the two graphs must be the same, since it is proportional to the total number of molecules.

The mathematical expression leading to the graph was originally derived for a single gas. Its use for reaction mixtures, whether in the gaseous or liquid phases, is a sensible extension of the original idea, but is diagrammatic rather than quantitatively precise.

Activation energy is shown on the diagram. This is explained below.

## Activation energy

The minimum collision energy needed for particles to react is called the **activation energy**, $E_a$. Particles that collide with energy greater than $E_a$ will react if their orientation is correct.

Activation energy is represented above on the Maxwell–Boltzmann distribution; the area to the right of it represents the number of molecules that possess the activation energy or more and which therefore could react. However, remember that it is the overall collision energy that matters.

At the higher temperature, the area to the right of $E_a$ increases, as does the number of successful collisions. Therefore, the rate increases. The $E_a$ is well to the right of the peak. Therefore, the proportion of successful collisions is very small.

Examination questions often ask for reference to a diagram such as that above — make sure you refer to the diagram in your answer.

## Catalysts

Catalysts change the mechanism of a reaction to one having a lower value of $E_a$. This means that the proportion of successful collisions at a given temperature increases and therefore the rate increases. Do not say that 'a catalyst lowers the activation energy'. The idea that the *mechanism* changes is very important.

At least one of the reactants must combine with the catalyst as an initial step. The complex formed then reacts with another reactant to give the products and regenerate the catalyst. The reaction profile for a catalysed reaction therefore has at least two humps, with an intermediate reactant–catalyst complex. This is shown in the diagram below.

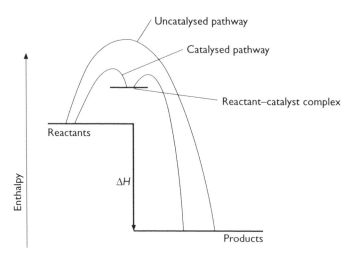

## Thermodynamic and kinetic stability

Methane and oxygen react only if ignited, to give carbon dioxide, water and heat.
$$CH_4 + 2O_2 \longrightarrow CO_2 + 2H_2O \quad \Delta H = -890 \, kJ \, mol^{-1}$$

The fact that $CO_2$ and water are at a lower energy than methane and oxygen means that $CO_2$ and water are **thermodynamically stable** with respect to methane and oxygen. The idea of thermodynamic stability is comparative — you must say that one mixture is stable *with respect to another*.

The reaction between methane and oxygen is immeasurably slow at room temperature. This is because the activation energy, $E_a$, is sufficiently high for there to be virtually no molecules that collide with this energy at room temperature. Methane and oxygen are therefore **kinetically stable** with respect to carbon dioxide and water.

Thermodynamic stability is a question of energetics, i.e. $\Delta H$; kinetic stability is a question of kinetics, i.e. $E_a$.

# Chemical equilibria

## Dynamic equilibrium

A reaction in dynamic equilibrium:

- is undergoing no net change, so the concentrations of all the substances are constant
- has a composition that can be approached starting from the reactants or the products
- is one in which the forward reaction (left to right as written conventionally) is happening at the same rate as the reverse reaction

A homogeneous equilibrium is one in which all the reagents and products are in the same phase.

An example of a liquid-phase equilibrium system is that involving ethanol, ethanoic acid, ethyl ethanoate and water.

$$CH_3CH_2OH + CH_3COOH \rightleftharpoons CH_3COOCH_2CH_3 + H_2O$$

This is an esterification reaction.

An example of a gas-phase equilibrium is the Haber process for the manufacture of ammonia.

$$N_2(g) + 3H_2(g) \rightleftharpoons 2NH_3(g)$$

## Change of conditions

### Effect of change in concentration

The esterification reaction is used as an example. If the concentration of either ethanol or ethanoic acid (or, in general, the substances on the left-hand side of the equation) is increased, the forward reaction occurs more rapidly until (new) equilibrium concentrations are established. The new equilibrium position will have a greater concentration of ethyl ethanoate and water (or, in general, the products — the substances on the right-hand side of the equation) than before. Thus, the yield is higher.

Reducing the concentration of the substances on the right-hand side, by removing them from the reaction vessel, will have the same effect of increasing the yield. A similar argument can be put forward for the reaction 'moving to the left', i.e. for the concentrations of substances on the left to increase if the concentration of the substances on the right-hand side is increased. In each case, the equilibrium position has moved in such a way as to *tend to* oppose the change of conditions.

In every case, *the important compositions are the equilibrium compositions.*

There is an infinite number of compositions that can give rise to equilibrium — the equilibrium composition is not a fixed one.

### Effect of change in pressure

The Haber process equilibrium is used as an example. Increasing the total equilibrium pressure moves the equilibrium composition towards the side with the smaller number of moles, i.e. the side with the smaller volume. In this case, the amount of ammonia would increase. A similar argument can be put forward for a decrease in pressure, which would move the equilibrium composition towards the reactants.

### Effect of changes in temperature

The effect of a change in the equilibrium temperature depends on whether the reaction, defined in the forward direction (left to right as written), is exothermic or endothermic. The ammonia synthesis mentioned above is exothermic in the forward direction.

$$N_2(g) + 3H_2(g) \rightleftharpoons 2NH_3(g) \quad \Delta H = -92 \text{ kJ mol}^{-1}$$

An increase in the equilibrium temperature moves the equilibrium position in the endothermic direction, i.e. to the left, so the yield of ammonia falls at higher temperatures. A similar argument can be made for endothermic reactions, where an increase in the (equilibrium) temperature moves the equilibrium position to the right.

#### Temperature control in an industrial process

A high yield of ammonia in the Haber process is favoured by a low temperature. The rate of reaction at a low temperature is also low.

In order to get a reasonable yield in a reasonable time, the temperature used is a compromise between the two conflicting demands — in practice, around 400 °C is satisfactory. Industrially, the Haber process is not operated as an equilibrium because the increase in time taken would not be justified by the extra yield.

# Industrial inorganic chemistry

Apart from the manufacture of aluminium, the technical details of industrial plant are not required.

## Ammonia manufacture

Ammonia is manufactured by the Haber process.

$$N_2(g) + 3H_2(g) \rightleftharpoons 2NH_3(g) \quad \Delta H = -92 \text{ kJ mol}^{-1}$$

| Condition | Value | Reasons |
|---|---|---|
| Temperature | 380–450 °C | • The reaction is exothermic, from left to right, so the temperature needs to be low for a good yield<br>• A sensible rate requires a high temperature<br>• The chosen temperature is a compromise that achieves a sensible yield in an acceptable time<br>• The yield per pass over the catalyst bed is about 15% |

| Condition | Value | Reasons |
|---|---|---|
| Pressure | 150 atm | • The number of product molecules is fewer than the number of reagent molecules<br>• A high yield is favoured by high pressure<br>• The chosen pressure is a compromise between costs (of which the highest by far is the fuel used to compress the gases) and acceptable yield |
| Catalyst | Fe/KOH | • KOH increases the effectiveness of the catalyst compared with iron alone |

The conditions used to obtain an economic yield in the Haber process are justified in terms of enthalpy change, equilibria and kinetics.

Uses of ammonia are:
• 80% — manufacture of fertilisers, including ammonium nitrate, ammonium sulphate, urea and liquid ammonia
• 7% — manufacture of nylon
• 5% — manufacture of nitric acid in the Ostwald process
• 8% — miscellaneous, including treatment of wood pulp

Annual production in the UK is 1.3 million tonnes; worldwide it is 140 million tonnes.

# Nitric acid manufacture

Nitric acid is manufactured by the Ostwald process. Ammonia (produced by the Haber process) is oxidised in air over a platinum/rhodium catalyst. The nitrogen monoxide produced is mixed with more air and cooled, resulting in oxidation to nitrogen dioxide, which is then absorbed in water.

$$4NH_3(g) + 5O_2(g) \rightleftharpoons 4NO(g) + 6H_2O(g) \quad \Delta H = -900 \text{ kJ mol}^{-1}$$

| Condition | Value | Reasons |
|---|---|---|
| Temperature | 900 °C | • The reaction is exothermic, from left to right, so temperature needs to be low for a good yield<br>• A sensible rate requires a high temperature<br>• The chosen temperature is a compromise that achieves a sensible yield in an acceptable time<br>• The yield per pass over the catalyst bed is about 96% |
| Pressure | 4–10 atm | • The number of product molecules is greater than the number of reagent molecules<br>• A high yield is favoured by low pressure<br>• A higher pressure reduces the physical size and hence the cost of the plant<br>• The chosen pressure gives an acceptable yield |
| Catalyst | Pt/Rh | • Rhodium increases the hardness of the catalyst and reduces catalyst loss resulting from hot spots on the catalyst surface |

The conditions used to obtain an economic yield in the Ostwald process are justified in terms of enthalpy change, equilibria and kinetics.

Uses of nitric acid are:
- 85% — manufacture of ammonium nitrate fertiliser
- 10% — manufacture of nitroaromatics for production of polyurethanes and dyestuffs
- 5% — manufacture of nylon

Annual production in Europe is 20 million tonnes; worldwide it is 60 million tonnes.

## Sulphuric acid manufacture

Sulphuric acid is manufactured by the Contact process. This process is the conversion of sulphur dioxide to sulphur trioxide.

$$2SO_2(g) + O_2(g) \rightleftharpoons 2SO_3(g) \quad \Delta H = -192 \text{ kJ mol}^{-1}$$

| Condition | Value | Reasons |
|---|---|---|
| Temperature | 430 °C | • The reaction is exothermic, from left to right, so temperature needs to be low for a good yield<br>• A sensible rate requires a high temperature<br>• The chosen temperature is a compromise that achieves a sensible yield in an acceptable time |
| Pressure | 2 atm | • A high yield is obtainable without the use of high pressure — the pressure needs to be enough to drive the gases through the plant |
| Catalyst | $V_2O_5$ | • There are four catalyst beds, giving > 99.5% conversion |

The sulphur trioxide is absorbed in 98% sulphuric acid which is kept at this concentration by addition of water and removal of the product acid.

The conditions used to obtain an economic yield in the Contact process are justified in terms of enthalpy change, equilibria and kinetics.

Uses of sulphuric acid are:
- 21% — manufacture of other chemicals
- 20% — manufacture of paints and pigments
- 19% — manufacture of detergents and soaps
- 40% — miscellaneous, including manufacture of dyes, plastics, salts, fibres and fertilisers (e.g. ammonium sulphate)

Annual production in the UK is about 2 million tonnes.

## Manufacture of inorganic fertilisers

Ammonium nitrate and ammonium sulphate are the main inorganic fertilisers. Ammonium nitrate is made from ammonia and nitric acid; ammonium sulphate from ammonia and sulphuric acid.

content guidance

# Manufacture of aluminium

Aluminium is extracted electrolytically in the Hall–Hèroult cell. The ore is bauxite, which contains mainly aluminium oxide, iron oxide and silicon dioxide.

## Purification of bauxite
- Bauxite is heated with 10% aqueous sodium hydroxide.
- The amphoteric aluminium oxide dissolves to give sodium aluminate; the acidic silica is a giant molecule and does not react with NaOH under these conditions; the basic iron oxide does not dissolve.
- Sodium aluminate is filtered and the filtrate of sodium aluminate is treated either with carbon dioxide or with a small amount of aluminium hydroxide. Aluminium hydroxide precipitates, is filtered off, washed and heated to give pure aluminium oxide.

## Electrolysis
Purified bauxite (5%), calcium fluoride (5%) and cryolite, $Na_3AlF_6$, are electrolysed at 900 °C in a carbon-lined steel pot with carbon anodes. The cathode is mostly the layer of molten aluminium on the floor of the pot.

Anode: $2O^{2-} \longrightarrow O_2 + 4e^-$
$C + O_2 \longrightarrow CO_2$

The anodes are therefore gradually eroded.

Cathode: $Al^{3+} + 3e^- \longrightarrow Al$

Uses depend on whether the metal is rolled, extruded or cast, but include building, transport and engineering construction.

Annual production in the UK is 250 000 tonnes; worldwide it is 19.5 million tonnes.

Aluminium production is expensive because of the cost of electricity — electrolysis is also a slow process. Nevertheless, its ease of working and wide range of uses makes extraction economic.

Recycling aluminium is significant because it saves some 90% of the cost of extracting the same amount from bauxite. It also reduces the amount of waste material requiring disposal.

# Manufacture of sodium hydroxide, chlorine and sodium chlorate(I)

Sodium hydroxide solution, chlorine and hydrogen are produced by electrolysis of sodium chloride solution in a cell with a titanium anode and steel cathode. A polymer membrane separates the cell compartments. It allows sodium ions to pass from the anodic to the cathodic compartment, but does not allow the passage of hydroxide or chloride ions.

Chlorine is produced at the anode, hydrogen at the cathode.

Uses of chlorine are:
- 33% — manufacture of chlorinated hydrocarbon solvents
- 27% — manufacture of chloroethene
- 13% — manufacture of inorganic chlorides including HCl
- 6% — manufacture of propene oxide
- 21% — miscellaneous, including water treatment and pesticide manufacture

Sodium chlorate(I) is made by reacting chlorine with sodium hydroxide solution.

$$2NaOH(aq) + Cl_2(aq) \longrightarrow NaCl(aq) + NaOCl(aq) + H_2O(l)$$

Sodium chlorate(I) is used as a bleach and as a germicide.

Questions
&
Answers

**T**he following questions are partly from one recent AS unit test and partly from previous A-level modular papers. Note that the format of the first set of questions — a unit test of duration 1 hour 15 minutes, worth 75 marks — predates the changes introduced from Summer 2003. Unit Test 2 has now been reduced to a length of **1 hour**, worth **60 marks**. The fundamental skills being tested remain the same. The supplementary questions have been adapted to make them appropriate to AS Unit 2.

Do not treat the answers as model answers or as rubber-stamp responses to be repro-duced without thought. The most important reason for studying chemistry is to *under-stand* it, not merely to repeat it parrot-fashion — you have to do more than simply aim for a good grade.

In some instances, the difference between an A-grade response and a C-grade response has been suggested. This is not always possible, since many of the questions are rather short and do not require extended writing.

I do not suggest that this section covers all the possible questions that could be asked on Unit Test 2 — examiners are more resourceful than that. However, there are examples of questions on each topic of Unit 2.

### Examiner's comments

Candidate responses to long-answer questions are followed by examiner's comments, preceded by the icon $\boldsymbol{e}$. They are interspersed in the answers and indicate where credit is due. They also point out common errors that lower-grade answers are prone to show.

# Set 1

# Unit Test 2, June 2001

## Question 1

(a) (i)  Explain the term *homologous series*.                                        (2 marks)

    (ii)  To which homologous series does ethene, $C_2H_4$, belong?                (1 mark)

(b) Draw the full structural formulae, showing all the bonds, for each of the following:

    (i)  the organic product of the reaction of ethene, $C_2H_4$, with aqueous
       potassium manganate(VII) and sulphuric acid                          (2 marks)

    (ii)  3,4-dimethyl-hex-2-ene                                                (2 marks)

    (iii)  a repeating unit of poly(propene)                                   (2 marks)

(c) Ethene reacts with hydrogen chloride gas to form $C_2H_5Cl$.

    (i)  What type of reaction is this?                                         (2 marks)

    (ii)  Give the systematic name for $C_2H_5Cl$.                              (1 mark)

**Total: 12 marks**

## Answer to Question 1

(a) (i) Compounds with the same general formula (or differing by $CH_2$) ✓ and having
similar chemical properties (or the same functional group) ✓.

☑ A C-grade answer might miss the second point. A third point could be that
homologues show a trend in physical properties.

    (ii) Alkenes ✓

(b) (i)

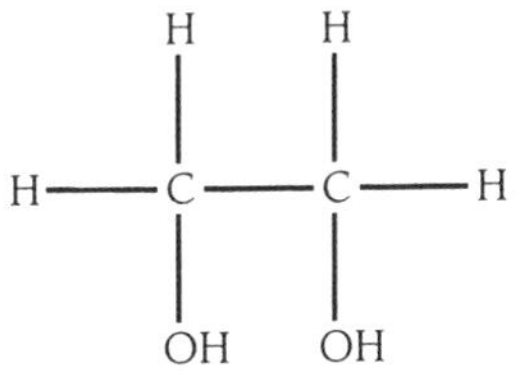

```
      H    H
      |    |
H——— C ——— C ———H
      |    |
     OH   OH
```

☑ Some candidates are mistaken in thinking that manganese should appear somewhere
in this formula. This structure gains 2 marks; if not all the covalent bonds were shown,
but the structure was otherwise correct, it would earn 1 mark.

    (ii)

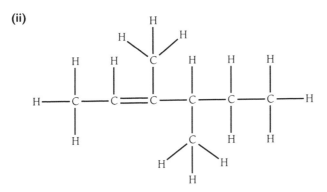

✍ The correct hexane framework earns 1 mark; the correct 3,4-dimethyl earns 1 mark. The methyl groups can be shown as $CH_3$. Grade-C answers often show valency errors about the C=C bond, having five bonds to C.

**(iii)**

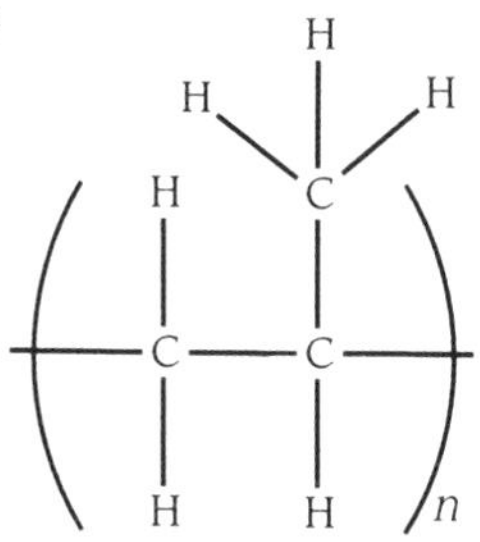

H
H    H
H    C
( C — C )
H    H    n

✍ C-grade answers often leave the double bond remaining in the structure.

**(c) (i)** Electrophilic ✓ addition ✓

✍ Both answers are free-standing. At AS, the mechanism is not examinable, but an understanding of the terms 'electrophilic' and 'addition' is necessary.

**(ii)** Chloroethane ✓

■ ■ ■

# Question 2

**(a) But-2-ene, $CH_3CH=CHCH_3$, exists as geometric isomers.**
   **(i)** **Draw the geometric isomers of but-2-ene.** (2 marks)
   **(ii)** **Explain how geometric isomerism arises.** (1 mark)
**(b) (i)** **Draw the structural formula of a compound which is an isomer of but-2-ene but which does not show geometric isomerism.** (1 mark)
   **(ii)** **Explain why the isomer drawn in your answer to (b) (i) does not show geometric isomerism.** (1 mark)

**Total: 5 marks**

## Answer to Question 2

**(a) (i)**

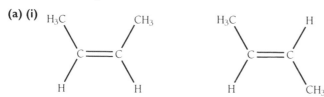

**(ii)** Restricted rotation about a C=C bond ✓

✍ This is, of course, not the only requirement — the groups on a given carbon atom in the double bond must be different. However, for a 1 mark answer, the second point is not needed.

**(b) (i)**

$$H_2C = CH — CH_2 — CH_3$$

But-1-ene

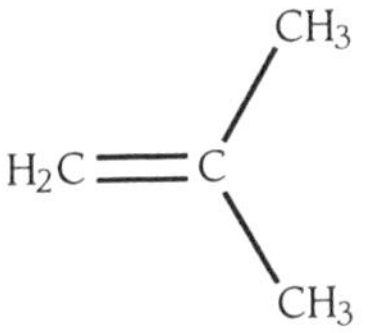

$$H_2C = C \begin{array}{c} CH_3 \\ \\ CH_3 \end{array}$$

2-methylpropene

$$\begin{array}{ccc} H_2C & — & CH_2 \\ | & & | \\ H_2C & — & CH_2 \end{array}$$

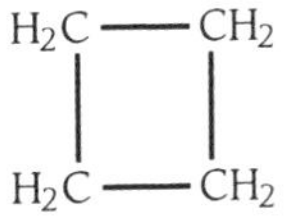

Cyclobutane

📝 The question does not specify that the compound must be an alkene, or that it should have a straight chain. Any of the above structures would therefore score. The presence of the cycloalkane does not mean that knowledge of such compounds is required by the specification, but it is a correct answer to the question and therefore would score. So would methylcyclopropane.

**(ii)** The groups on one of the carbon atoms in the double bond are the same ✓.

📝 This is correct if alkenes are drawn in answer to part (b) (i). An alternative reason is that there is no C=C bond in the cycloalkanes.

■ ■ ■

# Question 3

The rate of any chemical reaction is increased as the temperature is increased.
**(a) Draw a diagram of the Maxwell–Boltzmann distribution of molecular energies at a temperature $T_1$ and at a higher temperature $T_2$.** (3 marks)
**(b) Use your diagram and the idea of activation energy to explain why the rate of a chemical reaction increases with increasing temperature.** (4 marks)

**Total: 7 marks**

# Answer to Question 3

**(a)**

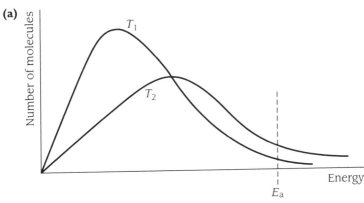

📝 To score the first mark, the curve for $T_1$ should be skewed and the correct shape (within reason), starting at the origin and not intercepting the x-axis at high energy. The other marks are for the curve for $T_2$ having a peak to the right ✓ and lower ✓ than that for $T_1$. The Maxwell–Boltzmann curve does have a particular shape, and a reasonable reproduction of it is expected. Common errors include too much symmetry, and the curve either starting part way up the y-axis or intersecting the x-axis, or both.

**(b)** Activation energy, $E_a$, is shown on the diagram well to the right of the peak ✓. The area under the curve for energies above $E_a$ for $T_2$ is higher than that for $T_1$ ✓ so there is a higher proportion of successful ✓ collisions, since collision energy is greater than $E_a$ for these molecules ✓.

⚠ The idea of **collision energy** is important, as is the ability to see kinetics in terms of particle interactions. Failing to refer to the diagram would lose a mark.

■ ■ ■

# Question 4

The reaction between sulphur dioxide and oxygen is a dynamic equilibrium:
$$2SO_2 + O_2 \rightleftharpoons 2SO_3 \quad \Delta H = -196 \text{ kJ mol}^{-1}$$
**(a)** Explain what is meant by *dynamic equilibrium*. (2 marks)
**(b)** In the table below, state the effect on this reaction of increasing the temperature and of increasing the pressure. (3 marks)

|  | Effect on the rate of the reaction | Effect on the position of equilibrium |
|---|---|---|
| Increasing the temperature | Increases |  |
| Increasing the pressure |  |  |

**(c)** This reaction is one of the steps in the industrial production of sulphuric acid. The normal operating conditions are a temperature of 450 °C, a pressure of 2 atmospheres and the use of a catalyst. Justify the use of these conditions:
(i) a temperature of 450 °C (3 marks)
(ii) a pressure of 2 atmospheres (2 marks)
(iii) a catalyst (1 mark)
**(d)** Give the name of the catalyst used. (1 mark)
**(e)** Give one large-scale use of sulphuric acid. (1 mark)

Total: 13 marks

## Answer to Question 4

**(a)** Forward and backward reactions occur at the same rate ✓. There is no net change in composition ✓.

**(b)**

|  | Effect on the rate of the reaction | Effect on the position of equilibrium |
|---|---|---|
| Increasing the temperature | Increases | Moves to left ✓ |
| Increasing the pressure | Increases ✓ | Moves to right ✓ |

🖉 The equilibrium moves in a direction that *tends* to oppose the imposed change. The changes are to the *equilibrium* conditions — the alteration in composition has no effect on the conditions, which are externally imposed.

**(c) (i)** The temperature needs to be high to give an acceptable rate ✓, but low to achieve an acceptable yield ✓. The temperature used is therefore an acceptable compromise/the temperature used is the optimum for the particular catalyst ✓.

**(ii)** High pressure increases yield but is not necessary, since an acceptable yield is obtainable at low pressures/the reaction needs just enough pressure to drive the gases through the catalyst bed(s) ✓. An increase in pressure would increase the yield but this would not offset the increase in costs ✓.

🖉 The yield is high because, in practice, four catalyst beds are used at differing temperatures. Also, low pressures are used because, at high pressure, $SO_3$ is extremely corrosive.

**(iii)** Increases reaction rate ✓

🖉 The implication from a cost/yield viewpoint is that the rate becomes acceptable at a lower temperature than would otherwise be the case.

**(d)** Vanadium(V) oxide/vanadium pentoxide ✓

🖉 Platinum can catalyse this reaction, but it is not used in industry and is not an acceptable answer.

**(e)** Oil refining ✓

🖉 Alternative correct answers include pigment manufacture, fertiliser manufacture and as an electrolyte in car batteries.

■ ■ ■

# Question 5

**(a)** State Hess's law. (2 marks)
**(b)** Define the term *standard enthalpy of combustion*. (3 marks)
**(c)** The equation for the combustion of ethanol in air is:

$$C_2H_5OH(l) + 3O_2(g) \longrightarrow 2CO_2(g) + 3H_2O(l)$$

The structural representation of this reaction is shown below.

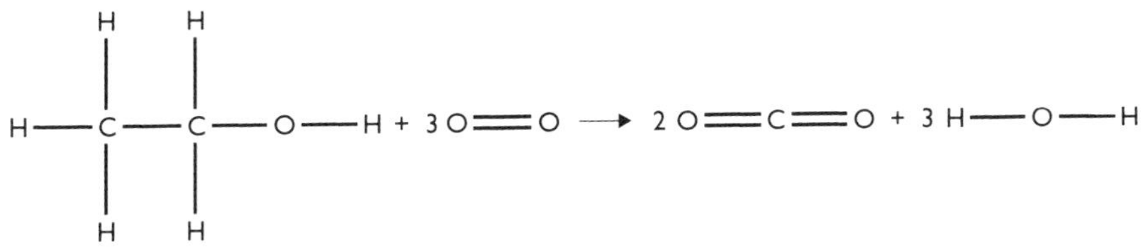

**(i)** Calculate the enthalpy change for this reaction, using the average bond enthalpy values given in the table below. (3 marks)

| Bond | Average bond enthalpy/kJ mol⁻¹ | Bond | Average bond enthalpy/kJ mol⁻¹ |
|------|-------------------------------|------|-------------------------------|
| C–H | +412 | C–C | +348 |
| C–O | +360 | O–H | +463 |
| O=O | +496 | C=O | +743 |

(ii) **Draw and label an enthalpy level diagram to represent this reaction.** (2 marks)

**Total: 10 marks**

## Answer to Question 5

**(a)** The heat/enthalpy change in a chemical reaction ✓ is independent of the route used to go from the reagents to the products ✓.

🗒 The term *energy* change should not be used; it refers to a reaction at constant volume, not constant pressure.

**(b)** The heat change per mole ✓ for the complete combustion of a substance in excess oxygen ✓ at 1 atm pressure and a stated temperature ✓.

🗒 In practice, a quoted temperature of 298 K would also get the credit, though this particular temperature is not part of the definition of the standard state. *Heat* change, not energy change, is very important. The energy change for a reaction is given the symbol $\Delta U$, and is measured at constant volume, not constant pressure.

**(c) (i)** There is no standard notation for the average bond enthalpy. Using D(X–X) to represent that for the X–X bond:

$\Delta H$ = [sum of bond energies of reagents] – [sum of bond energies of products] ✓
= [5D(C–H) + D(C–O) + D(C–C) + D(O–H) + 3D(O=O)] – [4D(C=O) + 6D(O–H)] ✓
= [(5 × 412) + 360 + 348 + 463 + (3 × 496)] – [(4 × 743) + (6 × 463)]
= –1031 kJ mol⁻¹ ✓

🗒 Note the heavy use of parentheses to separate out the various enthalpy calculations for each type of bond. The absence of such working is characteristic of C-grade answers and is a high-risk strategy. If the answer only is shown, and is wrong, there is no possibility of any salvage marks for intermediate steps. Additionally, it is important to be able to see what the chemical background to the calculation is. Examiners are better disposed to candidates whose work is transparent. Be careful to choose the correct values — it is quite common for candidates to use the C–O strength for the C=O bond, for example.

**(ii)**

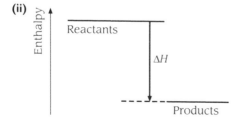

📝 There is 1 mark for the relative positions of the enthalpy levels and 1 mark for the energy barrier shown. If an arrow showing $\Delta H$ is required, it should have only one head pointing down; arrows with two heads are sometimes not accepted. For an endothermic reaction, the arrow should point upwards.

■ ■ ■

## Question 6

The enthalpy of combustion for each of two fuels is given in the table below.

| Fuel | Enthalpy of combustion/kJ mol$^{-1}$ |
|---|---|
| Hydrogen, $H_2$ | −280 |
| Octane, $C_8H_{18}$ | −5510 |

(a) Calculate the enthalpy change per unit mass for each of the fuels. (3 marks)
(b) Suggest, giving two reasons, which substance is the more useful as a fuel for motor cars. (2 marks)
(c) Suggest one disadvantage of using the fuel chosen as your answer to part (b). (1 mark)

**Total: 6 marks**

## Answer to Question 6

(a) Molar masses: hydrogen 2 g mol$^{-1}$; octane 114 g mol$^{-1}$ ✓
$\Delta H$ per unit mass for hydrogen: −280 kJ mol$^{-1}$/2 g mol$^{-1}$ = −140 kJ g$^{-1}$✓
$\Delta H$ per unit mass for octane: −5510 kJ mol$^{-1}$/114 g mol$^{-1}$= −48.3 kJ g$^{-1}$✓
(b) Hydrogen ✓: less pollution/greater energy per unit mass/renewable resource ✓✓
Octane: its density is much higher than that of hydrogen so a greater amount of fuel can be carried ✓. It is more readily available ✓.

📝 Both options are shown here. There are three marking points for the answer for hydrogen with a maximum 2 marks available. In questions like this, the reason is marked first, and, if satisfactory, the other mark is awarded. 'Hydrogen' alone would not score; it could be a guess.

(c) Hydrogen has to be pressurised and this is less convenient/more hazardous/so the pressure vessel is heavy ✓.
Octane is a more polluting fuel than hydrogen. For example, octane can give rise to carbon monoxide, while hydrogen produces only water ✓.

📝 'Hydrogen production uses electricity' and 'octane is non-renewable' are also acceptable answers, worth 1 mark each. The answer *must* relate to the fuel chosen in answer to part (b).

■ ■ ■

# Question 7

Aluminium metal is manufactured by a process in which purified bauxite, dissolved in molten cryolite, is electrolysed at 900 °C. Graphite electrodes and a current of about 120 000 amperes are used.

(a) (i)  Give the ionic equations for the reactions taking place at each electrode. (2 marks)

    (ii)  State which of these reactions is an oxidation process. (1 mark)

    (iii) Explain why the anodes need to be replaced frequently. (2 marks)

    (iv) Explain why an electrolyte of pure molten bauxite is not used. (2 marks)

(b) The production of aluminium is expensive.

    (i)  Explain why, despite this high cost, aluminium is manufactured in large quantities. (2 marks)

    (ii) Explain why it is worthwhile to recycle aluminium. (2 marks)

**Total: 11 marks**

# Answer to Question 7

**(a) (i)** Cathode: $Al^{3+} + 3e^- \longrightarrow Al$ ✓

      Anode: $O^{2-} \longrightarrow \frac{1}{2}O_2 + 2e^-$ ✓

The anode reaction produces the oxygen. The subsequent oxidation of the anode ($C + O_2 \longrightarrow CO_2$) is a redox reaction and not an electrochemical one. The cathode is commonly said to be graphite; in fact, it is mostly the layer of molten aluminium on the bottom of the cell.

**(ii)** The anode reaction, because it involves electron loss ✓.

Remember the association: anode, oxidation. This is true whether the cell is an electrolytic cell, as here, or an electrochemical cell (A2, Unit 4).

**(iii)** Liberated oxygen reacts with the anodes ✓ to give gaseous $CO_2$ which is lost ✓.

**(iv)** The melting temperature of bauxite is very high ✓ and it would be too expensive/too difficult to melt ✓.

It could be argued that the idea of 'pure bauxite' is strange — bauxite is the ore of aluminium and is of variable composition, but includes silica and iron(III) oxide. It can hardly be called 'pure'. Pure molten alumina is not used for the same reason given in the answer above. Its melting temperature is 2072 °C — well above the melting temperature of any metal that might be used to contain it. Iron, for instance, melts at 1535 °C.

**(b) (i)** Aluminium has many uses, based on either low density or high conductivity ✓, for which other metals cannot be substituted ✓.

    **(ii)** The main energy cost is in electrolysis of the alumina ✓; recycling the metal avoids this ✓.

# Question 8

(a) Predict the structural formula of the organic product from the reaction of
1-bromopropane, $CH_3CH_2CH_2Br$, with:
  (i)   aqueous potassium cyanide solution                                    (1 mark)
  (ii)  ammonia gas                                                            (1 mark)
(b) Give details of a chemical test you could do to distinguish between
2-chlorobutane and butan-2-ol, including the expected observations for
each compound.                                                                (2 marks)
(c) (i)  Draw the full structural formula, showing all the bonds, for the isomer
of butan-2-ol that is a tertiary alcohol.                                      (1 mark)
  (ii)  Give details of a chemical test you could do to distinguish between
butan-2-ol and its isomer drawn as your answer to part (c) (i) and
the observations you would expect to make.                                    (4 marks)
  (iii) Explain the chemistry involved in the test you described in part
(c) (ii).                                                                      (2 marks)

**Total: 11 marks**

# Answer to Question 8

**(a) (i)** $CH_3CH_2CH_2CN$ ✓

The question does not ask for all the bonds to be shown, so the answer given is satisfactory and unambiguous. This would not be true of $C_3H_7CN$, which could be either of two structures ($CH_3CH(CN)CH_3$ being the other) and is therefore not an acceptable answer.

**(ii)** $CH_3CH_2CH_2NH_2$ ✓

$CH_3CH_2CH_2NH_3{}^+Cl^-$ would also be an acceptable answer. The product could also be $(CH_3CH_2CH_2)_2NH$ or $(CH_3CH_2CH_2)_3N$. All of these would, in practice, be obtained from what is really a messy and not very useful reaction to give amines from halogenoalkanes.

**(b)** • To each compound, add phosphorus pentachloride ✓. Misty fumes indicate an –OH group, whereas the halogenoalkane does not react ✓.
  • Add potassium dichromate(VI) and sulphuric acid ✓. Alcohol turns it from orange to green, whereas the halogenoalkane does not react ✓.
  • Add potassium manganate(VII) and sulphuric acid ✓. Alcohol turns it from purple to colourless, whereas the halogenoalkane does not react ✓.
  • Heat each compound with sodium hydroxide solution and neutralise with nitric acid; then add silver nitrate solution ✓. The halogenoalkane gives a white precipitate, whereas the alcohol does not react ✓.

Four alternative answers are given. The test chosen can either be for the halogenoalkane or for the alcohol. Note that the colour *changes* must be specified, not just the final colour.

**(c) (i)**

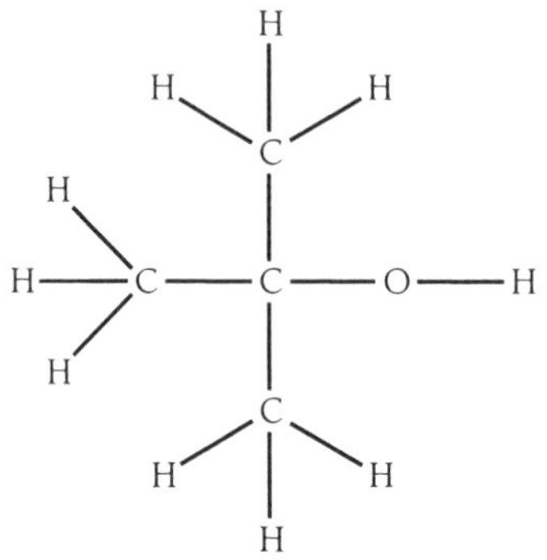

📝 The question asks for all the bonds. It is easier to draw such compounds if the methyl hydrogens are angled as shown above.

**(ii)** • Heat ✓ the alcohol with a mixture of potassium dichromate(VI) and sulphuric acid ✓. Butan-2-ol exhibits a colour change from orange to green ✓, whereas the tertiary alcohol does not react ✓.
   • Warm ✓ the alcohol with a mixture of potassium manganate(VII) and sulphuric acid ✓. Butan-2-ol exhibits a colour change from purple to colourless ✓, whereas the tertiary alcohol does not react ✓.

📝 Two alternative answers are given. Note that *both parts* of the colour change should be given. The 'heat' mark is conditional upon correct (or nearly correct) reagents. The reagents must be specified completely — 'acidified dichromate' is not enough to score.

**(iii)** The secondary alcohol gives a ketone ✓ in this oxidation reaction. Tertiary alcohols cannot be oxidised under these conditions, since there is not a removable hydrogen atom on the tertiary carbon atom ✓.

# Supplementary questions

## Question 1

(a) Some values of standard enthalpies of combustion are shown in the table below.

| Substance | C(graphite) | $H_2(g)$ | Ethane $C_2H_6(g)$ |
|---|---|---|---|
| $\Delta H_c^{\ominus}$/kJ mol$^{-1}$ | –393.5 | –285.8 | –1560 |

   (i) Define the term *standard enthalpy of combustion*. (3 marks)

   (ii) Complete the following thermochemical equation for the standard enthalpy change of combustion of ethane:

$$...C_2H_6(...) + ...O_2(...) \longrightarrow ...CO_2(...) + ...H_2O(...) \quad \Delta H^{\ominus} = ...$$ (3 marks)

   (iii) Use the data to calculate the standard enthalpy change of formation of ethane. Draw a Hess's law cycle as part of your answer. (3 marks)

(b) Consider the reaction:

$$C_2H_6(g) + Cl_2(g) \longrightarrow C_2H_5Cl(g) + HCl(g) \quad \Delta H^{\ominus} = -112.6 \text{ kJ mol}^{-1}$$

This reaction does not proceed at room temperature in the absence of light, but reacts rapidly when exposed to a bright light. Use these facts to illustrate the concepts of thermodynamic and kinetic stability. (2 marks)

Total: 11 marks

## Answer to Question 1

(a) (i) Heat change per mole ✓ for the complete combustion of a substance in excess oxygen ✓ at constant pressure and a stated temperature ✓.

(ii) $1C_2H_6(g) + 3\frac{1}{2}O_2(g) \longrightarrow 2CO_2(g) + 3H_2O(l) \quad \Delta H^{\ominus} = -1560 \text{ kJ mol}^{-1}$

There is 1 mark for the coefficients, 1 mark for the states of matter and 1 mark for the enthalpy change value.

(iii)

$$2C + 3H_2 \xrightarrow{\Delta H_f} C_2H_6$$

$$2\Delta H_c(C) \qquad 3\Delta H_c(H_2) \qquad \Delta H_c(C_2H_6)$$

$$[2CO_2 + 3H_2O] \qquad ✓$$

$$\Delta H_f = 2\Delta H_c(C) + 3\Delta H_c(H_2) - \Delta H_c(C_2H_6) \checkmark$$
$$= (2 \times (-393.5)) + (3 \times (-285.8)) - (-1560)$$
$$= -84.4 \text{ kJ mol}^{-1} \checkmark$$

(b) The products are thermodynamically unstable with respect to the reactants since the reaction is exothermic ✓. The reactants are kinetically stable since the activation energy is too high ✓ to permit observable reaction at room temperature.

💡 Note that thermodynamic stability is used in a comparative comment referring to both the reagents and the products.

■ ■ ■

# Question 2

(a) **Write an equation, the enthalpy change for which would be the enthalpy of formation of zinc sulphide, ZnS.** (2 marks)

(b) **In the smelting of zinc ores, the following reaction occurs:**

$$ZnS(s) + 1\tfrac{1}{2}O_2(g) \longrightarrow ZnO(s) + SO_2(g) \quad \Delta H^{\ominus} = -441 \text{ kJ mol}^{-1}$$

**Use this, together with the data below, to calculate a value for the enthalpy of formation of ZnS.**

**Data:** $Zn(s) + \tfrac{1}{2}O_2(g) \longrightarrow ZnO(s) \quad \Delta H^{\ominus} = -348 \text{ kJ mol}^{-1}$

$S(s) + O_2(g) \longrightarrow SO_2(g) \quad \Delta H^{\ominus} = -297 \text{ kJ mol}^{-1}$ (3 marks)

(c) **One way of utilising the large quantities of sulphur dioxide formed in reactions such as that in (b) is to convert it into sulphur trioxide thus:**

$$2SO_2(g) + O_2(g) \rightleftharpoons 2SO_3(g) \quad \Delta H^{\ominus} = -98 \text{ kJ mol}^{-1}$$

**State and explain the effect on the position of equilibrium of:**

(i) **increasing the temperature at constant pressure** (3 marks)

(ii) **increasing the total pressure at constant temperature** (2 marks)

**Total: 10 marks**

## Answer to Question 2

(a) $Zn(s) + S(s) \longrightarrow ZnS(s)$ ✓✓

💡 If the states are omitted then 1 mark would be lost. This implicitly tests the knowledge that the enthalpy of formation is the heat change for the production of a compound from its elements.

(b) $\Delta H_f = \Delta H_c(Zn) + \Delta H_c(S) - \Delta H_c(ZnS)$ ✓
$= (-348) + (-297) - (-441)$ ✓
$= -204 \text{ kJ mol}^{-1}$ ✓

💡 This shows that calculations involving heats of combustion can be found outside organic chemistry.

(c) (i) The reaction is exothermic, left to right ✓. An increase in temperature causes the equilibrium to shift from right to left ✓, since this tends to oppose the change in conditions ✓.

(ii) The equilibrium moves to the side with the smaller number of molecules ✓, which is from left to right ✓.

💡 In both (c) (i) and (c) (ii), the mark for direction of movement requires some explanation.

■ ■ ■

# Question 3

(a) The graph below represents the Maxwell–Boltzmann distribution of molecular energies at a temperature $T_1$ K.

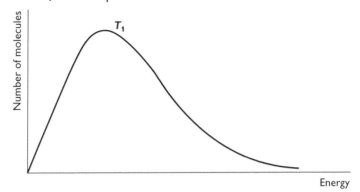

(i) Sketch on the same axes the curve that shows the distribution of molecular energies at a higher temperature, $T_2$ K. $T_2$ is approximately 20 K greater than $T_1$. (2 marks)

(ii) Use these graphs to explain how the rate of a gas phase reaction changes with increasing temperature. (4 marks)

(b) For a gaseous reaction, state and explain what effect the addition of a catalyst would have on:

(i) the energy distribution of the gas molecules (2 marks)

(ii) the activation energy for the reaction (2 marks)

(iii) the rate of the reaction (2 marks)

**Total: 12 marks**

# Answer to Question 3

(a) (i)

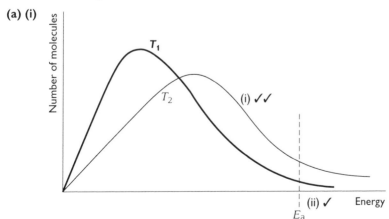

The peak for the $T_2$ graph must be lower and to the right of that for $T_1$, with the areas under the graphs more-or-less the same.

(ii) The area under the graph at $T_2$ above this energy is greater than that for $T_1$ ✓. This leads to a greater number of successful collisions ✓, which leads to an increase in rate.

The mark for the activation energy value is conditional upon it being not too near the peak, i.e. well to the right. The proportion of successful collisions in a reaction system is actually extremely small — perhaps only one in $10^{15}$ or so.

(b) (i) No effect ✓, since the energy distribution for a given gas depends only on the temperature ✓.

(ii) The catalyst provides an alternative mechanism ✓, which has a lower activation energy than the uncatalysed pathway ✓.

The idea of a different mechanism or different pathway is very important. The common statement that 'the activation energy is lowered' is not correct. An activation energy is a mechanism-specific quantity, so the mechanism must alter if $E_a$ is to be different.

(iii)The rate increases ✓, since a greater proportion of molecular collisions will have an energy greater than the catalysed $E_a$, so there will be more successful collisions ✓.

■ ■ ■

## Question 4

(a) **Sodium hydroxide is manufactured by an electrolytic process using a membrane cell.**
  (i) **What is used as the electrolyte?** (1 mark)
  (ii) **Of what materials are the anode and cathode made?** (2 marks)
  (iii) **Give an equation for the reaction occurring at each of the electrodes.** (2 marks)
  (iv) **Give one reason why it is necessary to have the two electrodes in separate compartments.** (1 mark)
  (v) **Write an equation for the overall cell reaction.** (2 marks)
(b) **Give one large-scale industrial use for each of the following:**
  (i) **chlorine** (1 mark)
  (ii) **hydrogen** (1 mark)

**Total: 10 marks**

## Answer to Question 4

**(a) (i)** Concentrated aqueous sodium chloride ✓

'Brine' would be a simplified answer. However, the examiner might not think this enough, as it does not show whether the candidate knows what 'brine' is. Seawater, for example, is salt solution and is 'briny', but is too dilute for use in the membrane cell. The answer given removes any possibility of misunderstanding.

**(ii)** The anode is titanium ✓; the cathode is steel ✓.
**(iii)** Anode: $2Cl^-(aq) \longrightarrow Cl_2(g) + 2e^-$ ✓
    Cathode: $2H^+(aq) + 2e^- \longrightarrow H_2(g)$ ✓
**(iv)** It prevents reaction of chlorine with sodium hydroxide ✓.

🖉 It also prevents the hydrogen and chlorine from mixing, though at room temperature they would not react. The above point has always been considered more important, since in the manufacture of sodium chlorate(I) the membrane is omitted to allow the following reaction to occur:

$$2NaOH + Cl_2 \longrightarrow NaOCl + NaCl + H_2O$$

**(v)** $2NaCl(aq) + 2H_2O(l) \longrightarrow 2NaOH(aq) + H_2(g) + Cl_2(g)$

🖉 There is 1 mark for the correct species and 1 mark for balance. Note that this reaction cannot occur directly.

**(b) (i)** Sterilisation of water/manufacture of PVC/bleaching ✓

🖉 There are other possible answers, but note that 'water purification' is not correct — chlorinated water is not purer in a chemical sense, but it is sterile. 'Swimming pools' is not an acceptable answer — nobody swims in chlorine!

**(ii)** Manufacture of HCl/manufacture of margarine/manufacture of ammonia/ rocket fuel ✓.

🖉 Other uses could be listed, but 'hot air balloons' is not one of them — they use hot air, not hydrogen. Few candidates seem to realise this.

■ ■ ■

# Question 5

**Low-density poly(ethene) is used for packaging and plastic bags. The exothermic reaction by which poly(ethene) is made is shown by the following equation:**

$$nC_2H_4 \longrightarrow (C_2H_4)_n$$

**(a) Write the structural formulae, showing all the bonds, of:**
  **(i)  ethene** (1 mark)
  **(ii) poly(ethene), showing three repeating units** (2 marks)
**(b) Draw a representative length of the molecule of poly(2-methylpropene), showing three repeating units.** (2 marks)
**(c) (i)  Write the structural formula, showing all covalent bonds, of the product obtained by reacting 2-methylpropene with bromine.** (1 mark)
  **(ii) Write the structural formula of the compound formed by the reaction of aqueous sodium hydroxide with the product of the reaction in (c) (i).** (1 mark)

**Total: 7 marks**

# Answer to Question 5

**(a) (i)**

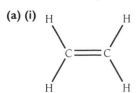

(ii)

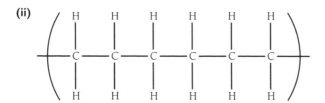

✐ There is 1 mark for showing six carbon atoms and 1 mark for an implication of extent beyond these six carbons.

(b)

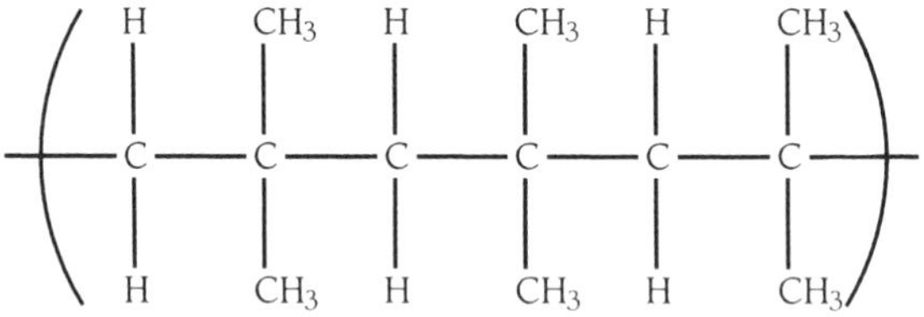

✐ There are 2 marks for the structure as drawn with six carbon atoms in the chain. One mistake could still leave 1 mark, but if any of the methyl groups were included in the chain, the answer would score zero. Including substituent atoms in the chain is a common error in representing the polymerisation of substituted alkenes. The chain is made up from doubly bonded carbon atoms in the monomer only. Everything else forms a side-chain on the polymer.

(c) (i)

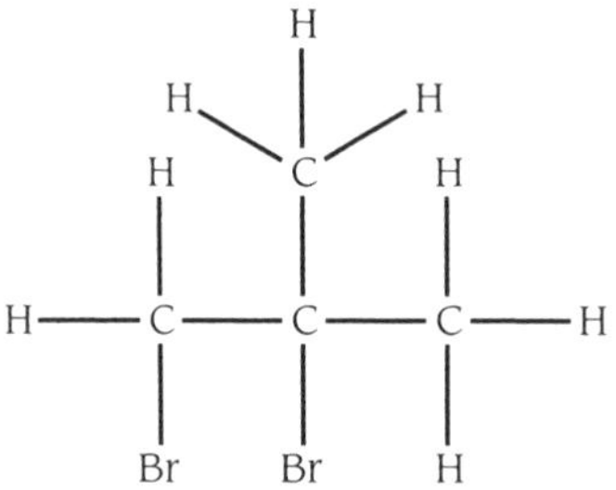

(ii)

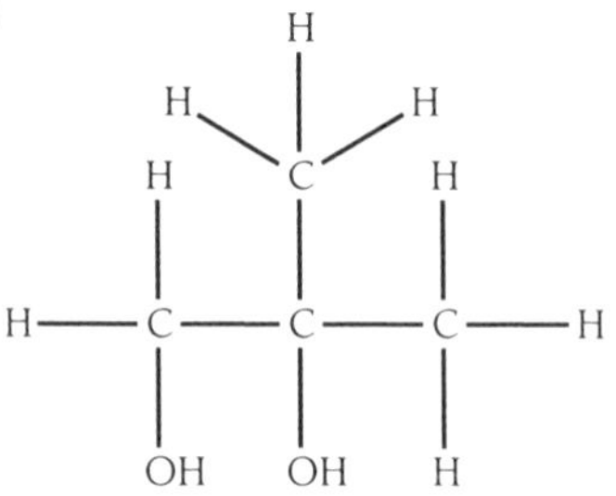

✐ The bromine atoms are displaced by hydroxide ions in a nucleophilic substitution reaction.

◼ ▨ ◼

# Question 6

The equilibrium reaction

$$2SO_2(g) + O_2(g) \longrightarrow 2SO_3(g)$$

is used in the manufacture of sulphuric acid, using $V_2O_5$ as a catalyst.

(a) (i) Given that the enthalpies of formation of $SO_2$ and $SO_3$ are −297 and −395 kJ mol⁻¹ respectively, calculate the enthalpy of reaction, $\Delta H$, for the forward reaction, assuming that it goes to completion. (2 marks)

(ii) State and explain what happens to the equilibrium position of this reaction as the temperature is raised. (3 marks)

(iii) The temperature that is used in practice for the industrial process is a balance between economics and chemistry. Suggest three reasons that determine the choice of an operating temperature of around 450 °C. (3 marks)

(iv) What effect does the catalyst have on the position of equilibrium in this reaction? (1 mark)

(v) Sketch an enthalpy level diagram for this reaction, showing on it both uncatalysed and possible catalysed routes. (4 marks)

(b) Explain the effect on equilibrium position of increasing the concentration of oxygen in the system at constant temperature. (2 marks)

Total: 15 marks

# Answer to Question 6

(a) (i) $\Delta H = 2\Delta H_f(SO_3) - 2\Delta H_f(SO_2)$ ✓
= (−395 × 2) − (−297 × 2) = −196 kJ mol⁻¹ ✓

As usual, the chemical background is expected, as given in the first line. The use of 'kJ mol⁻¹' sometimes causes confusion — as written here, it means for the molar quantities given in the equation, that is, for the production of two moles of sulphur dioxide.

(ii) The equilibrium moves in the endothermic direction ✓, which is from products to reactants ✓ since this is the direction that tends to oppose the change in the external conditions ✓.

Note that the changed conditions are equilibrium conditions. The movement of the equilibrium does not reduce the temperature again.

(iii) The rate of the reaction is enough to give an acceptable yield of sulphur trioxide, in a sensible time, at 450 °C ✓. The yield obtained is enough to cover the costs at 450 °C ✓. The cost of maintaining the temperature at 450 °C is acceptable ✓.

Few industrial processes that are equilibria are allowed to reach equilibrium because the extra yield obtained is not usually justified by the extra time needed to come to complete equilibrium.

**(iv)** None ✓

📝 Catalysts affect only rate, not equilibrium position.

**(v)**

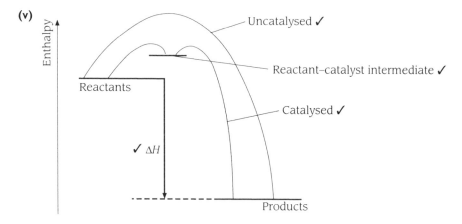

📝 The double hump for the catalysed reaction is expected — there must be a catalyst–reactant intermediate of some sort, otherwise there is no reason for the catalyst to be there.

**(b)** Equilibrium moves in the direction that tends to reduce the oxygen concentration ✓, that is, from left to right ✓.

■ ■ ■

# Question 7

Consider the following series of reactions, and then answer the questions that follow.

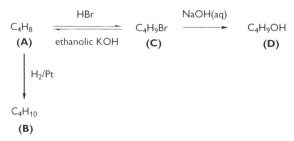

**(a) (i)** Compound **(A)** exists in two stereoisomeric forms. Draw them, and state the feature of the molecule that makes this isomerism possible. (3 marks)
   **(ii)** Give a simple chemical test for the functional group present in **(A)**, stating what you would see. (2 marks)
   **(iii)** **(A)** is more reactive than **(B)**. Suggest in terms of the nature of the bonding in these compounds why this is so. (2 marks)
   **(iv)** What type of reaction is the conversion of **(A)** to **(C)**? (2 marks)
   **(v)** What type of reaction is the conversion of **(C)** to **(A)**? (1 mark)

**(b) (i)** The reaction of **(C)** to give **(D)** is a nucleophilic substitution. What is meant by the term *nucleophile*? (2 marks)

**(ii)** Give the structural formula for **(D)**. (2 marks)

**(iii)** Give a simple chemical test for the functional group in **(D)**, stating what you would see. (2 marks)

**Total: 16 marks**

## Answer to Question 7

**(a) (i)**

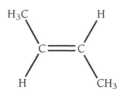

Restricted rotation about the C=C bond ✓

☑ There is also 1 mark for each structure.

**(ii)** Bromine water ✓ changes from yellow/orange to colourless ✓.

☑ Note the difference between *colourless* (no colour) and *clear*, which means see-through and can be any colour. Confusion between the two is common.

**(iii)** The C=C bond has easily accessible electron density in the π-bond ✓. The π-bond is weaker than the σ-bond between the atoms in B ✓, which must be broken for reaction to occur ✓.

**(iv)** Electrophilic ✓ addition ✓

**(v)** Elimination ✓

**(b) (i)** A species with a lone pair of electrons ✓ that seeks positive centres in the attacked molecule ✓.

**(ii)**

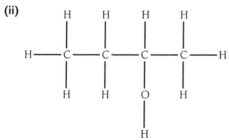

☑ There is 1 mark for the structure being an alcohol, and 2 marks for it being the correct alcohol. The question does not ask for all the bonds to be shown, but this is a fail-safe approach.

**(iii)** Add phosphorus pentachloride ✓. Steamy (acidic) fumes ✓ are produced.

☑ 'Acidic fumes' alone would not score, since you cannot *see* that they are acidic.

## Question 8

Two types of reaction in organic chemistry are nucleophilic substitution and electrophilic addition. Define the terms:

(a) nucleophile         (2 marks)
(b) electrophile        (2 marks)
(c) substitution       (1 mark)
(d) addition         (1 mark)

**Total: 6 marks**

## Answer to Question 8

**(a)** A species with a lone pair of electrons ✓ that seeks positive centres in the attacked molecule ✓.
**(b)** A species that is electron deficient/has a positive charge ✓ and which seeks areas of high electron density in the attacked molecule ✓.
**(c)** A reaction in which one atom or group is replaced by another atom or group ✓.
**(d)** A reaction in which the product molecule contains all the atoms from both the reactant molecules ✓.

## Question 9

The pleasant smell that betrays the making of toast or of caramel comes from the compound hydroxymethylfurfural, which is a product of heating sugars. The structure of the molecule is shown below:

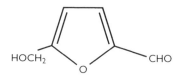

HOCH$_2$      O      CHO

(a) (i)   **What would you see if this compound were shaken with a solution of bromine dissolved in an organic solvent?** (1 mark)
(ii)  **Suggest a structure for the product obtained from this reaction.** (2 marks)
(iii) **Suggest a reagent that you could use and the observations you would make to show the presence of a hydroxyl group in hydroxymethylfurfural.** (2 marks)
(b)  **If hydroxymethylfurfural is heated with potassium dichromate(VI) solution which has been acidified with dilute sulphuric acid, the compound X obtained contains 46.1% carbon, 2.56% hydrogen and 51.3% oxygen by mass. The ring structure remains intact.**
(i)   **Calculate the empirical formula for X.** (2 marks)
(ii)  **Draw the structural formula for X, given that its relative molecular mass is 156.** (3 marks)

**(c)** Hydroxymethylfurfural can react with hydrogen in the presence of a catalyst to give compound **Y** which has the structure shown below:

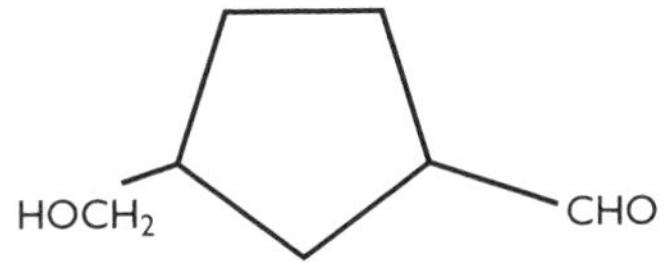

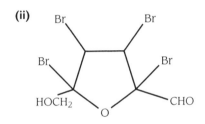

What volume of hydrogen would be required to convert 3.15 g of hydroxymethylfurfural into compound **Y**? (The molar volume of any gas at the temperature and pressure of the experiment is 24 dm³; the relative molecular mass of hydroxymethylfurfural is 126.)   (3 marks)

Total: 13 marks

## Answer to Question 9

**(a) (i)** The yellow/orange solution of bromine is decolorised/becomes colourless ✓.

☞ Note the difference between *colourless* (no colour) and *clear*, which means see-through and can be any colour. Confusion between the two is common.

**(ii)**

Br, Br
Br, Br
HOCH₂  O  CHO

☞ This structure scores 2 marks. If only one double bond had been involved in the addition then just 1 mark would have been awarded. This is simply an unusual way of examining the test for an alkene.

**(iii)** Add phosphorus pentachloride ✓. Steamy (acidic) fumes ✓ are produced.

☞ 'Acidic fumes' alone would not score, since you cannot see that they are acidic.

**(b) (i)**

|          | Divide by r.a.m.      | Divide by smallest    | Ratio of atoms |
|----------|-----------------------|-----------------------|----------------|
| Carbon   | 46.1/12 = 3.84        | 3.84/2.56 = 1.5       | 6              |
| Hydrogen | 2.56/1 = 2.56         | 2.56/2.56 = 1         | 4              |
| Oxygen   | 51.3/16 = 3.20        | 3.20/2.56 = 1.25      | 5              |

Therefore, the empirical formula is $C_6H_4O_5$ ✓✓.

☞ A calculation such as this is more likely to appear in Unit Test 3, since it is related to practical chemistry, but it is of course Unit 2 material, which is why it is here.

**(ii)** The relative molecular mass of $C_6H_4O_5$ is: $(6 \times 12) + 4 + (5 \times 16) = 156$ ✓. So the empirical formula is also the molecular formula ✓. The structure is shown below.

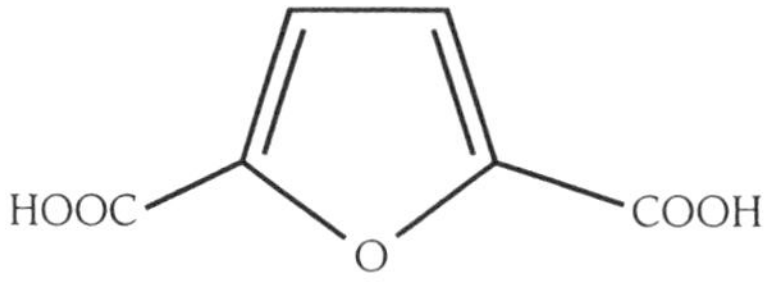

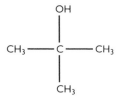

HOOC ―― COOH ✓

💡 This question requires you to see that both the primary alcohol group on the left of the original compound and the aldehyde group on the right will oxidise under the conditions stated to give carboxylic acids.

**(c)** Amount of hydroxymethylfurfural = 3.15 g/126 g mol$^{-1}$= 0.025 mol ✓
Amount of hydrogen = 2 × 0.025 mol = 0.05 mol ✓
Volume of hydrogen = 0.05 mol × 24 dm$^3$ mol$^{-1}$
= 1.2 dm$^3$ ✓

💡 In calculations, *all* the working should be shown. Not to do so is a high-risk strategy. If the answer is wrong and there is no working, all the available credit evaporates.

▪ ▪ ▪

## Question 10

One of the isomers of $C_4H_{10}O$ is the alcohol 2-methylpropan-2-ol, which has the following structural formula:

OH
|
CH$_3$ ―― C ―― CH$_3$
|
CH$_3$

**(a)** There are three other *structural* isomers of $C_4H_{10}O$, which are also alcohols. Draw their structural formulae. (3 marks)
**(b)** Describe a test to show that each of the isomers in (a) contains an –OH group. (2 marks)

**Total: 5 marks**

## Answer to Question 10

**(a)**

CH$_3$CH$_2$CH$_2$CH$_2$OH ✓

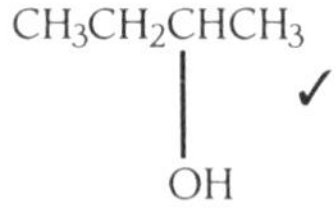

CH$_3$CH$_2$CHCH$_3$
|
OH ✓

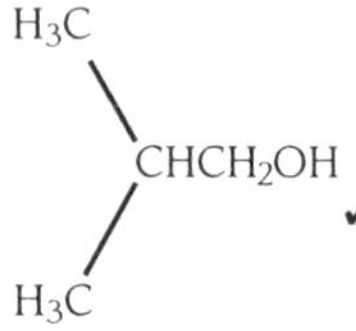

H$_3$C
\
CHCH$_2$OH ✓
/
H$_3$C

**(b)** Add phosphorus pentachloride ✓. Steamy (acidic) fumes ✓ are produced.

💡 'Acidic fumes' alone would not score, since you cannot *see* that they are acidic.

## Question 11

Cars are fitted with catalytic converters in order to reduce the pollution caused by the combustion of petrol. Potential polluting gases include carbon monoxide, nitrogen monoxide and unburnt hydrocarbons. The first two compounds are removed by passing the hot gases over a platinum catalyst:

$$CO(g) + NO(g) \longrightarrow CO_2(g) + \tfrac{1}{2}N_2(g) \quad \Delta H = -373 \text{ kJ mol}^{-1}$$

In the absence of a catalyst, this reaction is extremely slow.

(a) Define the term *activation energy*. (2 marks)

(b) Comment on the relative value of the activation energy of this reaction compared with the much faster reaction of nitrogen monoxide with oxygen. (1 mark)

**Total: 3 marks**

## Answer to Question 11

**(a)** The minimum collision energy ✓ that the reacting molecules must have in order to react ✓.

Relating the activation energy to the molecules involved in the reaction, rather than some vague notion such as 'the energy needed to start a reaction' (common in C-grade answers), is very important. It shows some understanding of collision theory.

**(b)** The slower the rate at a given temperature the higher is the activation energy ✓.